VIBRATIONAL HEALING

IN THE SAME SERIES:

Principles of Acupuncture
Cathy Hopkins
Principles of Aromatherapy
Cathy Hopkins
Principles of Art Therapy
Daniel Brown
Principles of Chinese Herbal Medicine
John Hicks
Principles of Chinese Medicine
Angela Hicks
Principles of Colour Healing
Ambike Wauters and Gerry Thompson
Principles of Feng Shui
Simon Brown
Principles of Kinesiology
Maggie La Tourelle and Anthea Courtenay
Principles of Native American Spirituality
Dennis Renault and Timothy Freke
Principles of Palmistry
Lilian Verner-Bonds
Principles of Reflexology
Nicola Hall
Principles of Reiki
Kajsa Krishni Boräng
Principles of Self-Healing
David Lawson
Principles of Shamanism
Leo Rutherford
Principles of Shiatsu
Chris Jarmey
Principles of Stress Management
Vera Peiffer
Principles of Tai Chi
Paul Brecher
Principles of Yoga
Sara Martin
Principles of Your Psychic Potential
David Lawson

THORSONS
PRINCIPLES
OF

VIBRATIONAL HEALING

AMANDA COCHRANE
AND CLARE HARVEY

Thorsons
An Imprint of HarperCollins*Publishers*

Thorsons
An Imprint of HarperCollins*Publishers*
77–85 Fulham Palace Road,
Hammersmith, London W6 8JB

Published by Thorsons 1998
1 3 5 7 9 10 8 6 4 2

A catalogue record for this book
is available from the British Library

ISBN 0 7225 3503 1

Printed and bound in Great Britain by
Caledonian International Book Manufacturing Ltd, Glasgow

CONTENTS

Introduction   vii

1   The History of Vibrational Healing   1
2   Body Energies   15
3   Sound Therapy   29
4   Light and Colour   49
5   Transmitting Healing Vibrations   67
6   Vibrational Medicines   81
7   Vibrational Healing in Action   105

Resources   109

INTRODUCTION

V ibrational healing is a kind of energy medicine. It springs from the belief that each of us has an energy or life force which influences our wellbeing, and that everything vibrates with energy. Although we cannot see or touch this energy, like the air we breathe it is essential to life. This invisible energy can be enhanced and rebalanced by naturally occurring vibrations such as light, colour, sound and the energies of plants, flowers and crystals, to restore harmony in mind, body and spirit.

The origins of vibrational healing can be traced back to the mists of time. Over 5,000 years ago wise men became aware that there is more to human beings than meets the eye. They spoke of a universal energy pervading all living organisms, a concept that formed the basis of many ancient philosophies and healing methods.

Throughout history different peoples such as the Aztecs, Ancient Egyptians, Native Americans and Australian Aborigines have used forms of vibrational healing. Traditional Chinese and Japanese medical systems also view life force as something that can be harnessed for healing.

Feelings of wellbeing are inextricably linked to this energy. When we have abundant, free-flowing and balanced energy, we enjoy vitality, good physical health, mental clarity and real contentment and fulfilment. Disturbances in the body's energy field often accompany and are thought to underlie all kinds of discomforts and dissatisfaction.

Nowadays stress and ever-increasing exposure to man-made vibrations such as artificial lighting and the noise of traffic are primarily responsible for throwing our energy systems out of balance. Is it any wonder that we dream of escaping to a desert island to soak up the sun's natural rays and listen to the soothing sound of waves lapping against the shore? Human beings are attuned to the energetic vibrations of nature and nothing else can nourish and revitalize life force in the same way.

Vibrational healing uses a variety of invisible wave forms to restore energetic equilibrium. Each therapy has its own healing frequency or energy waveband.

Light and colour, sound and music, crystals and gemstones, plants and flowers can all be used as catalysts for healing. Some healers can transmit healing vibrations through themselves to others.

The benefits of vibrational healing can be far-reaching. As well as healing the body and helping to release deeply ingrained tensions, vibrational healing causes a profound revitalization at all levels: mind, body and spirit.

Vibrational therapy is increasingly finding favour with people who sense that there is more to good health than the absence of illness. True wellbeing means having boundless energy, feeling emotionally balanced and being at ease with yourself and the kind of life you are living. When mind, body and spirit are nourished life becomes full of meaning and purpose.

The resurgence of interest in vibrational healing comes at a highly significant time. The ancient prophecies of Vedic seers (6,000 to 8,000 years ago), the Aztecs, Hopi Indians, Mayans, Tibetans and Aborigines refer to a golden age which is said to occur every 25,000 years, and predict that the next era of enlightenment will dawn around the year 2000. Recent translations of sacred texts and inscriptions found on Mayan stone discs suggest this information was recorded all those years ago for the benefit of future generations.

Legend also has it that there is a concentration of energy, rather like an electromagnetic sheath of light, that encircles the world. This energy can be likened to the photon belt, a band of light energy particles discovered by scientists in 1961, in the vicinity of the Pleiades. It is said that the photon belt is moving ever closer to our own solar system and that sometime between the year 2000 and 2012 the Earth is scheduled to slip into it. No one knows for sure what this event may bring. Some predict that it will heighten the vibrations upon the planet, resulting in the dawn of super-consciousness, so bringing to pass the ancient prophesies of a golden age.

Many healers believe, therefore, that it is extremely important to enhance the vibrational patterns of the human body to enable us to cope with the changes this event will bring. Vibrational healing has a major part to play at this time of transition.

THE HISTORY OF
VIBRATIONAL HEALING

Vibrational healing – the notion that all living organisms are infused with a life force or energy that is influenced by other energetic vibrations – can be traced back in its various guises to ancient civilizations around the world. The traditional medical systems of the Chinese, Japanese and Tibetans, the Ancient Egyptians and Greeks, the Native Americans and Australian Aborigines feature at least one, if not several different vibrational therapies and remedies. Over the centuries physicians and healers have discovered many different ways of using light, sound and other vibrational wave forms in ways that can bring about healing.

MYTHICAL LANDS

The inhabitants of some mythical places had a profound knowledge of vibrational healing.

The most ancient land of mythology is Lemuria or Mu, said to have been in existence some 500,000 years ago. Located in an area now covered by the Pacific Ocean, Lemuria was reputedly like the Garden of Eden, a vibrant land where all kinds of exquisite flowering plants flourished. The people could attune themselves to the Earth's natural energies and they lived in

harmony with nature. They were said to be highly sensitive individuals who could sense the energies of plants, flowers, animals and other people, and they found ways to harness particular vibrations for healing.

It is possible that flower remedies – essences encapsulating the energies of flowers – were first used therapeutically in Lemuria. They may have been taken as an aid to spiritual development and attaining enlightenment. The Lemurians allegedly harnessed the energetic vibrations of gems and crystals, primarily for spiritual expansion and growth.

The subtle energies (the therapeutic vibrational qualities) of herbs were valued for healing. By attuning themselves to the energetic vibrations of plants, the Lemurians were able to discern their healing properties. They realized that sage can help to dissolve energy blockages resulting from negative thought patterns, trauma and shock, which is why it was traditionally used as a cleansing herb. (In contrast, modern day herbalists use herbs according to their pharmacological properties: sage has antiseptic and anti-inflammatory properties and is commonly used to relieve period pain and menopausal problems.) Sage was also burned as an offering to the four corners of the Earth – north, south, east and west – in a purification ceremony that is still practised by Native Americans.

In Indonesia the tradition of being able to sense the vibrations emitted by plants and herbs survives today. Typically the healer enters a state of meditation or mindfulness to increase his sensitivity to the vibrational qualities of a plant. Simultaneously he develops a capacity to sense sickness or disharmonious patterns within the physical body. This enables him match the appropriate herb to the vibrational flaw in the body.

According to myth, Lemuria gave way to Atlantis, a civilization which became far more technologically advanced than its predecessor.

It has been suggested that vibrational healing has its true origins in Atlantean culture. Numerous flower essences, gem remedies and homeopathic remedies were developed to treat illnesses that emerged for the first time in Atlantis.

The Atlanteans would have been aware that the energy of sunlight has a profound influence on all living cells. By creating flower essences and gem elixirs they were able to fuse the vibrations of nature with the subtle energetic properties of sunlight.

The Atlanteans are particularly famed for their knowledge of the healing power of crystals: they knew that the colours produced when sunlight passes through a crystalline prism can be used for healing purposes. Some speculate that crystals were grown artificially to achieve specific qualities and sizes for different uses such as laser surgery. A number of crystalline devices were utilized in the diagnosis as well as the treatment of disease.

Legend has it that when Atlantis crumbled, survivors fled to other parts of the globe taking with them their knowledge of vibrational healing. This is why different peoples throughout the world share similar healing philosophies and practices.

ANCIENT EGYPT

The power of Ancient Egyptian healer-physicians is legendary. According to Homer, the Greek historian and storyteller, their skills in medicine exceeded those of any others. There is little doubt that they knew of the therapeutic power of vibrational healing.

To understand the Ancient Egyptian approach to healing, we need to know a little about their view of man and his place in the universe. To the Ancient Egyptians, everything was interlinked. Man was a microcosm of the universe, which was charged with subtle energy currents: the cosmic 'uranian' forces and the subterranean 'telluric' forces. Like the Ancient Chinese philosophers, the Ancient Egyptians were intrigued by the relationship between Earth and the cosmos, and great emphasis was placed upon establishing a connection with the sun and stars. They regarded this link as fundamental to a sense of wellbeing.

All the temples in Ancient Egypt were aligned to particular stars and all the sacred buildings were of cosmic design. Great pyramids and obelisks were built to reach up to the heavens. The pyramidal points of these awe-inspiring constructions were capped with gold or electrum to reflect the sun's rays across the land. It is said that great quartz crystals were placed on the top of certain pyramids which scattered coloured rays in different directions.

The sun was worshipped as a god named Ra. The Ancient Egyptians knew that light rays emitted by the sun are essential for life on Earth. They undoubtedly recognized the healing power of its component colours, too. There were healing temples of light and colour at Heliopolis in Egypt as well as in early Greece, China and India.

The Ancient Egyptians referred to medicine and healing as 'the necessary art' and it was clearly designed to cater for the mind, body and spirit.

Originally all cures were thought to have been revealed by the gods and interpreted by Thoth, god of medicine and science, and author of a 42-volume encyclopedia which was part of the great library at Alexandria.

Throughout the ancient world the ability to heal or practise medicine was usually either a gift, or a vocation handed down from father to son or from master to pupil.

In Ancient Egypt there were various classes of healers. The most highly regarded medicine was temple medicine. Training was strict and secrecy was imposed to preserve knowledge.

The most renowned of all the Egyptian healers was Imhotep, whose powers were so extraordinary that he became one of the most popular deities of healing. Born about 3000 BC, during the reign of King Zoser, Imhotep was a sage and scribe, astronomer, magician, physician and architect of the famous step-pyramid of Sakkara, near Memphis.

Some physicians were skilled in the art of healing with their hands, one of the most ancient and traditional techniques of amplifying and transmitting energy. Some temple healers were capable of tapping into telluric and cosmic forces and directing them by sweeping their hands over the patient's body, without touching him or her. This healing process is depicted in bas-reliefs. In the villages there were bonesetters who could heal simple fractures and sprains simply by laying their hands on the wounded parts.

There is little doubt that the Ancient Egyptians also harnessed the healing power of flowers. They did, after all, perfect the art of aromatherapy and so it is likely that they used flower remedies in other ways too.

ANCIENT GREECE

Many currents of Ancient Egyptian thought found their way to Ancient Greece. Pythagoras and Hippocrates both spoke of healing energies: Pythagoras said that a central fire in the universe was the prime cause of creation and that from this originated all healing energy. Hippocrates called this healing energy 'vis medicatrix naturae'. Around 500 BC the Pythagoreans were the first to record the aura as a luminous body.

Asklepios was the personification of divine healing powers and the guardian of patients. He gave and preserved health and relieved disease, by wiping away illness with his hands or just touching the patient. He built temples in places of extraordinary

natural beauty so that patients would be nurtured by the harmonious energies of their surroundings. These sanctuaries were safe, tranquil places in which the individual could explore the centre of his being: those who wished to be healed were expected to rectify their way of life and ultimately take responsibility for their own wellbeing.

Music played an important part in healing rituals. Both Plato and Aristotle tell us that the Ancient Greeks developed the theory that sound in the form of music or tone can have a healing effect. There are tales of Greek musicians who could recognize a person by their unique note or sound, and of great healers who could tune into the inner harmony of a patient, then play one note on a lyre which totally healed him or her.

Pythagoras established that there is a strong connection between the senses and music, and that sound contributes 'greatly to health if used in an appropriate manner'. He combined and composed 'diatonic, chromatic and enharmonic melodies' with particular rhythms, and the positive vibrations of these melodies alleviated negative emotions, especially sorrow, rage, pity, pride and anger. Unfortunately we have no idea what this music sounded like.

Aristotle reported that flute music could stimulate the emotions and release pent-up tension. Casiodorus believed that Aeolian music could treat mental disorders and help to induce sleep, while Lydian music was suitable for children and could 'soothe the soul when oppressed with excessive care'.

NATIVE WISDOM

Scattered across the globe are tribespeople who believe that everything in nature possesses a spirit or kind of energy.

Shamanism dates back thousands of years and embraces this notion. The principles of shamanism are common to many cultures including the Native Indians of North and South America, the people of Tibet and Indonesia, the Australian Aborigines, the Laplanders of the Arctic Circle, the Altai of Siberia, and many tribes throughout Africa.

These people share the belief that it is important to establish good relationships with the nature spirits if you wish to be healthy in mind, body and spirit. The shaman, or medicine man or woman, is a highly revered member of the community blessed with the special gift of being able to communicate with the nature spirits and call upon their help to heal the sick. Traditionally, through rhythmic dancing and drumming, the shaman enters a trance in which he is able to contact these spirits. Typically the medicines he uses are energetically charged stones and energy-purifying plants. By working with the subtle energies of nature the shaman is practising a form of vibrational healing.

Whilst the shamanic ideal of living in harmony with nature is shared by different cultures, each has evolved their own way of doing this.

In many South American cultures the planet Earth is given the name *pachamama*, meaning sacred Earth mother. Pachamama is a living being with physical, astral and spiritual bodies, which interconnect. She is a nurturer, and a spiritual mother who holds the secrets of the Universe within her.

The Ancient Incas of Peru referred to the Earth energies as the *Apus*. The Apus guard the Earth and when a person is born they take responsibility for his or her development. They are the intermediaries between humans and the Earth. The Inca shamans worked with these energies or spirits for guidance, resolution of disputes and all healing.

The Q'ueros are a Quechua speaking people living in the mist-shrouded mountains of south central Peru. They are the descendants of Incan high priests or shaman and the keepers of ancient mystical traditions. They have managed to keep their cultural and spiritual beliefs alive, untainted by the influences of the outside world, for over 400 years. One of these traditions is the *despacho* ceremony, where offerings are made to pachamama, in thanks and honour of her energies.

The Q'ueros speak of two realities: the *panya* and the *yoqe*. Panya is everything associated with the ordinary world or physical reality; yoqe is all that belongs to the extraordinary world or the invisible reality – the enigma of the energies that are present in all beings: people, animals, plants and stones. They refer to the subtle energy that exists in all people as *animu*. At birth this energy, which comes from pachamama, enters the body through the top of the head.

All the skills that the Q'ueros priests or shamans (known as *pago*) learn are to do with the harmonious interplay of energies. The shaman's gift is the ability to heal his people's relationship with the cosmic forces in ways that bring harmony and balance into their lives.

Q'uyas are power stones are used by the Pag'o shamans for healing. Each stone holds energies placed there by nature, and the most powerful come from areas very high in the Andes where lightning strikes the Earth. As well as having their own energies, each stone is endowed with a healing function by the shaman. They can be used to cleanse heavy energetic vibrations from the body arising from negative thoughts and feelings.

ANIMAL ENERGY

The South American Indians regard contact with animal guardians as especially important for healing and restoring harmonious relationships with Father Sky, Mother Earth and all the elements. Guidance, strength and knowledge is gained from tuning in to animal spirits or subtle energies.

In the jungles of eastern Peru there are shamans who use a mind-expanding jungle vine called ayahuasca in their ceremonies. This visionary plant expands awareness in such a way that it enables the shamans to see and hear animal spirits in their visions. The spirits of snakes, tigers, jaguars, eagles, condors, crocodiles or dolphins usually present themselves: these animals are believed to possess special energies that can cure the sick. Ayahuasca also helps to release negative vibrations held in the body as a result of destructive thought processes and all forms of trauma.

NEGATIVE VIBRATIONS

In shamanic traditions there is much reference to evil spirits which prey on mental, emotional and vital energy. These energy parasites are often nothing more sinister than our own negative thought patterns.

An ancient Tibetan myth (originating from the Bon religion) recounts the origin of negativity and the causes of illness. It tells of five demons which manifest five poisons (actually referred to in this religion as the five passions): ignorance, jealousy, pride, attachment and hatred. The Tibetan shamans communicate with the disturbed spirits, especially the five great demons, to persuade them not to create problems and confusion.

The Tibetan shamans see illness as an energy imbalance that humans create between themselves and all existence. Humans disturb the spirits of the five elements – space, air, fire, water and earth – the four seasons, and the spirits of nature – sky, sun, moon, mountains, rocks, rivers and plants. We do this by digging up the earth, polluting the air, rivers and lakes, and so forth.

The shaman determines whether a person has an energetic imbalance or is being provoked by negative energy (or a demonic spirit). He then performs purification rituals: he summons powerful life force energy from all over the universe and condenses it into syllables which he speaks, and introduces into the disturbed person's heart through her crown chakra (located on the crown of the head), to strengthen her life force. The life force may also be revived by recanting a mantra (words of natural power) of the life deity, which calls upon the blessings of the buddhas, the magic power of all the spirit protectors and guardians.

The shamans of the Altai people living in Siberia refer to vital energy or life force as *chula*. They see chula as one of nine souls, and as important for health and normal development. It is thought that a person with a predisposition to openness is vulnerable to evil spirits or negative energies which may 'steal their chula'. When this happens the life force is weakened and the person becomes sick. The shaman can perform soul retrieval rites which rekindle the life force and restore the patient's health and wellbeing.

INDIA

Over 5,000 years ago wise men or yogis living in the remote Himalayan mountains spoke of a universal energy. Known as *prana*, this energy is still seen by yogis as the basic constituent of all life. Prana, the breath of life, moves through all things and brings vitality to them. The yogis were aware that this energy is affected by different forms of vibrations. Their ancient Sanskrit language is actually comprised of words which set up a sympathetic vibration in the body. The word for tiger, for example, houses the essential energy of the tiger. When they spoke this word, people would be calling upon the spirit or energy of the animal.

The yogis developed a system of natural medicine known as Ayurveda, whose principles have spread throughout Asia and has been handed down from generation to generation. It is still alive today and has recently kindled much interest in the Western world.

One of the oldest Ayurvedic practices is chanting and reciting silent mantras. The repetition of sacred sounds maintains and promotes wellbeing in mind, body and spirit, because of the effect on the body's energy systems.

The ancient texts of Indian yogic literature describe various energy systems associated with the body. According to the sages the physical body is energized and coordinated by an energetic subtle body called the *etheric* body. Within this etheric body are vital energy centres known as *chakras*, which are linked with each other and the nervous system by lines of life force. The chakras gather and hold different forms of energy, and can alter their vibrations so that they can be used for different healing purposes.

Chanting conditions the chakras so that energy flows smoothly throughout the body. When the body's energies are balanced and free-flowing, the mind is still. When the mind is free of distracting thoughts and the disruptive effects of emotions such as anxiety, fear and guilt, it is possible to enjoy greater access to the soul or higher self. In other words, meditative techniques for bringing peace of mind also revitalize and rebalance the body's energies. The yogis also discovered that certain movements and body positions encourage prana to flow through the body. Yoga is the classical example of this ancient form of energizing exercise.

Common to Eastern medical and mystical tradition is the idea that the universe is a living organism, a rhythmic vibrational field, infused and permeated with life force. During the third millennium BC the Ancient Chinese philosophy of Taoism emerged which holds that every living organism, as well as the universe itself, is infused and permeated with a rhythmic vibrational energy known as *qi* or *chi*. The Japanese call this energy *ki*, and in India it is referred to as *prana*.

Taoism teaches that if man lives in harmony with the laws of nature, his whole system will be balanced mentally, emotionally, physically and spiritually, because qi will flow freely and evenly through the body.

Problems arise when we consider ourselves to be separate and superior to nature. Nowadays processed and over-refined foods, polluted air and a lack of healthy exercise often distance us from the natural way of life and stifle qi. Emotional stress, an over-indulgent or frenetic lifestyle, injury and illness also block the flow of vital energy. The Taoists suggest that energy imbalances are responsible for us becoming susceptible to emotional upsets such as anger, irritability, sadness and fear. These negative feelings can weaken bodily systems and make us vulnerable to disease.

The early Eastern philosophers devised ways of promoting the free-flow of energy to preserve wellbeing and instil peace of mind. Exercise regimes based on slow, rhythmic movements such as Tai Chi and Qi Gong were devised to balance qi. Today millions of people in China and Japan perform these slow moving, free-flowing movements as part of their daily routine. Various types of massage to encourage the swift and even movement of qi have also been developed. As in India, meditative techniques such as chanting were found to affect qi.

In Japan there is also an ancient tradition of drumming which opens up the chakras and stimulates the flow of ki energy.

BODY ENERGIES

To understand how vibrational healing works we have to acknowledge the existence of an energy or life force that permeates all living beings. We cannot see or touch this energy, but like the air we breathe, it is essential to life.

For many people living in the West, the idea that there is more to human beings than meets the eye is hard to imagine. In other regions of the world however, especially the Far East and Asia, this view is widely accepted. The traditional medical systems of the Chinese, Japanese, Tibetans, Indonesians, Australian Aborigines and Native Americans all regard this energy as something tangible that can be influenced for better or worse.

SCIENCE SUPPORTS
THE ENERGY THEORY

The idea that all things are infused with energy is not as mystical as it may seem. Modern physics is beginning to add credibility to what wise men believed all those years ago. In this century it has become old-fashioned to think of things as solid objects, as Newton and his colleagues in the late 17th and early 18th centuries did.

Scientists now believe that our world is composed of energy fields and vibrational wave forms that constantly interact with one another. Indeed, some view the universe as a vast web of inseparable energy patterns.

There is scientific evidence that human beings possess their own energy fields. Dr Saxton Burr, an American researcher and Professor of Anatomy at Yale University Medical School in the mid–1940s, shattered conventional belief when he put forward what he called the electrodynamic theory of life. He suggested that all physical forms, be they human, animal, vegetable or mineral, are held together and governed by electro-magnetic fields of energy which he called life-fields. Although these fields are invisible, their effect can be reproduced by placing a magnet under a card and sprinkling iron filings over it. The filings form a pattern which reflects the magnetic force field.

The life-field, as Dr Burr called the energy field, is like a flexible jelly mould which produces a shape, and the physical body is akin to the jelly. Although physical forms are separate entities, they are linked in terms of energy to all other bodies.

The human electromagnetic energy field can be measured with sensitive instruments such as vacuum tube voltmeters. It responds to the energetic impulses associated with different kinds of thoughts: positive thinking strengthens the energy field, and negative thoughts weaken it. Certain vibrational wave forms in the environment also influence our energy field. Fluctuations in the Earth's electromagnetic field, for example, have a direct effect on our vitality and health.

Western medical science has made extensive studies of the Earth's electromagnetic field. Careful monitoring has shown that there is a link between field flow (the strength of intensity of the electromagnetic currents or waves) and the occurrence of viral and bacterial epidemics. In short we are locked into a life-field which links and affects us all.

For centuries healers have been working with different energy systems described by ancient medical and esoteric teachings. To grasp the principles of vibrational healing it is helpful to know a little about these.

THE AURA

Since time immemorial artists and mystics have seen auras. Ancient Indian sculptures, Aboriginal rock paintings and Native American totem sculptures all show figures surrounded by light or with lines emanating from their bodies. Around 500 BC the Pythagoreans of Ancient Greece were the first to describe the aura as a luminous body. They believed its light could produce a variety of effects in humans.

The aura is an invisible, yet luminous kind of radiation which resembles a halo surrounding the physical body. It has parallels with the electromagnetic force field, in that it surrounds the body with a field of biomagnetic energy, which acts as a barometer of the body's physiological pro-cesses. All life forms possess an aura, composed of vibrational frequen-cies emitted by fundamental particles of the body.

Human auras vary widely in size, density and colour and consist of different coloured light rays, each associated with an organ of the body. The vibrancy and hue of an aura depends on the person's spiritual evolution as well as his or her general health. The more balanced and healthy you are, the greater your auric field.

The shape, colour and strength of the rays vary from person to person, reflecting their personality, mood, emotions and expe-riences. For example, a lot of red in an aura indicates the pres-ence of anger, while blue relates to idealism. Those who have auras with soft edges are susceptible to the influence of others, while a hard, distinct outline may indicate a person with a defensive or aggressive attitude resulting from deep insecurity.

The aura is a reflection of the immune system. The stronger your aura, the more resilient you are to illness. An aura can radiate some three or four feet from the body, its energy infusing the whole subtle body system (*see below*). In ill health, the aura shrinks back close to the body in an attempt to conserve vital energy.

THE SUBTLE BODIES

The subtle bodies are layers of energy. They can be visualized as seven bands of light encasing and emanating from the physical body. Each layer vibrates at a slightly different frequency and can be defined by its colour, density and appearance. Each has a specialized function and influences various emotional, mental and physical processes.

- *Etheric body* or *lining* – the first subtle body, which lies between the physical and other subtle bodies to sustain a dynamic equilibrium between them. An energetic replica of the physical body containing a blueprint of all the organs.
- *Emotional body* – the seat of the emotions. When the emotional body is in balance it brings emotional security and stability.
- *Mental body* – reflects mental activity and enables us to think clearly and rationally. It contains the structures of our thoughts and ideas.
- *Astral body* – encapsulates the entire personality. When it is in balance we are more likely to have an intuitive understanding of events and the flow of life.
- *Causal body* – the seat of willpower, it facilitates interaction with other people and events, allowing us to fulfil our personal destinies. The gateway to higher consciousness.

- *Celestial* or *Soul body* – houses our spiritual essence and is, in a sense, the higher self which allows the soul to move freely through us.
- *Spiritual* or *Illuminated body* – a fusion of the whole subtle anatomy with the physical body. Our basic energetic blueprint resides here.
- *Etheric envelope* – forms a protective outer coating around the subtle bodies.
- *Immunofluidum* – contains and transports qi.

Like other energy systems, the subtle bodies can become congested with inappropriate energetic vibrations. In the mental body, congestion usually takes the form of half-formed, unclear thoughts which mount up like piles of rubbish and prevent clear thinking. Similarly, unexpressed desires and emotions cloud the emotional body. Lack of exercise and sunshine, or an excess of junk food can muddy the etheric body. Each body can also become over-stimulated and this can lead to a variety of health problems.

Finally, a condition known as lack of coordination can occur between the mental and emotional bodies, between the emotional and etheric or more commonly between the etheric and the physical bodies. When the etheric body is not properly linked to the physical you are likely to experience chronic fatigue and in extreme cases frailty.

THE MERIDIANS

Traditional Chinese Medicine sees subtle energy (qi or chi) as taking the form of vibrational waves. The qi flows along a system of channels known as *meridians*. The first reference to this energy network is found in the *Nei Ching* or *Yellow Emperor's Classic of Internal Medicine* which is around 4,500 years old.

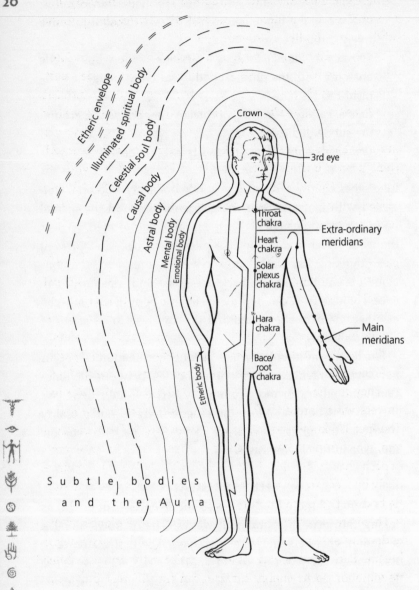

Etheric envelope

Illuminated spiritual body

Celestial soul body

Causal body

Astral body

Mental body

Emotional body

Crown

3rd eye

Throat chakra

Heart chakra

Solar plexus chakra

Hara chakra

Bace/ root chakra

Etheric body

Extra-ordinary meridians

Main meridians

Subtle bodies and the Aura

The subtle anatomy of mankind

PRINCIPLES OF VIBRATIONAL HEALING

These channels form an intricate web through the body, like a second nervous system. It connects the physical body to the subtle energy bodies surrounding it.

There are 12 pairs of meridians, and each pair is associated with a different organ system or function, such as the heart, lungs or liver. There are also a further eight energy channels known as the extraordinary meridians which hover in between the etheric and physical bodies. They act as an energy reservoir and are closely connected with our vitality and state of mind. Their prime function is to feed the main meridians with qi. Traditional Chinese Medicine maintains that good health and peace of mind are inextricably linked to the smooth and even flow of qi through the body.

THE CHAKRAS

Eastern medical and mystical traditions share the notion that special energy centres known as *chakras* play a vital role in moving energy around the body. There are seven major chakras which are inextricably linked to the meridian system.

The chakras act as energy transformers, simultaneously receiving, assimilating and transmitting various types of energy. They can be imagined as many-petaled, vibrantly coloured flowers which are attached by invisible threads to the spine. The 'petals', known as *nadis*, are woven into the nervous system, which runs through the spine. They distribute the energy of each chakra into the physical body. The chakras are continuously opening to receive information about the state of the subtle bodies, and closing again, rather like anemones.

There are seven chakras which govern major glands in the endocrine system and influence physical and psychological health. Each chakra has its own 'pulse rate' and can alter its vibration so its energy can be used for different purposes. Some vibrate very quickly, others more slowly, depending largely on the ways in which we use and regard our bodies. Each chakra also has its own note (*see page 29*).

If one chakra is not functioning properly it affects those above and below it. Ideally the top chakras should vibrate faster and more subtly than the lower ones, but this is not always the case and heavy vibrations can appear in all the centres.

CHAKRAS AND THEIR PROPERTIES

Chakra	Colour	Physical associations	Psychological influences
1st or Root	Red	Large intestine, legs, feet, skeletal structure. Imbalance linked to obesity, constipation, haemorrhoids, sciatica, arthritis, knee problems, poor circulation in legs and extremities.	Connection with the Earth, survival, releasing of emotional tension. Imbalance linked to accident proneness, dependency, identity crisis, weak ego.
2nd or Hara	Orange	Male and female reproductive organs, bladder, circulation. Imbalance linked to low back trouble, reproductive problems, premenstrual syndrome, urinary problems.	Sexuality, creativity. Imbalance linked to weak personality, depression, hysteria, inability to be sexually intimate.
3rd or Solar plexus	Yellow	Adrenal glands, solar plexus, spleen, pancreas, stomach. Imbalance linked to problems of the stomach, anorexia, diabetes, blood glucose, anaemia, allergies, obesity.	Feeling empowered and in control. Imbalance linked to addictive and compulsive behaviour, excessive anger or fear, manic depression, sleep problems, psychosomatic conditions.

Chakra	Colour	Physical associations	Psychological influences
4th or Heart	Green	Heart, thymus gland, immune system, lungs. Imbalance linked to circulatory and respiratory problems, upper back troubles, child-hood diseases.	Understanding, compassion, unconditional love. Imbalance is linked to inner conflict, self-destructive ten-dencies, relationship problems, feelings of alienation, loneliness.
5th or Throat	Blue/Turquoise	Thyroid, parathyroid, lymphatic system, immune system, neurological system. Imbalance linked to teeth, ear, neck and shoulder problems, sore throats, bronchial problems, hearing and speech difficulties.	Trust, expression, creativity, communi-cation. Imbalance linked to an inability to express oneself verbally, stuttering, doubting the sincer-ity of others.
6th or Third eye	Indigo	Pituitary gland, left-brain hemisphere, central nervous system. Imbalance linked to nervous upsets, eye and vision problems, headaches, sinusitis.	Clarity and insight, interest in spirituali-ty. Imbalance linked to confusion, poor memory, inability to focus, paranoia, feeling detached from reality.
7th or Crown	White	Pineal gland, right-brain hemisphere, ancient mammalian brain. Imbalance linked to migraine headaches, pituitary problems, epilepsy	Intuition, to be open and have faith, connection to higher energies or realms. Imbalance linked to being gullible, having nightmares, multi-ple personalities, being spiritually closed.

HOW THE ENERGY SYSTEMS INTERACT

The energy systems described above are all interlinked (*see illustration page 20*). There is a constant interplay between them, so they effectively function as an energetic whole. They can be visualized as translucent layers held in place with thin membranes which separate yet allow the energies to diffuse into one another.

All seven subtle bodies enter and leave the body through chakras, which tie in with the meridian system. The meridians pass through the organs of the body. The extraordinary meridians link up with the subtle bodies and the aura, interfacing with the whole subtle anatomy system.

The entire energy system is in a continuous state of motion – the different energies are like swirling mists of colour and light interacting and receiving information from each other. They are constantly inter-changing, redistributing and rebalancing themselves.

DISTURBING THE ENERGY BALANCE

In a perfect world we would all have abundant energy and our energy systems would function smoothly. This state of energetic harmony and balance is associated with health, vitality, emotional stability, mental clarity, contentment, fulfilment and a sense of being on the right path in life. The energy systems usually function smoothly in newborn babies, but as we proceed on our journey through life the systems are thrown off balance for numerous reasons.

SHOCK AND STRESS

Emotional distress in its many guises has a devastating effect on the subtle energy system. The impact of shock is like the ripples caused by a pebble hurled into a still pond, which spread through the water. Shock waves reverberate in the same way through the subtle anatomy. Long slow shock and prolonged stress have the same effect, their effects just take longer to show.

Whereas a pond becomes still again once the pebble has dropped to the bottom and the ripples die down, disturbances in the energy system remain unless steps are taken to bring it back into balance. The subtle bodies are thrown out of alignment and sometimes spill into one another. Any disruption in the subtle bodies eventually filters down to the physical body, where a range of symptoms are triggered, depending on which part of the body is affected.

Physical shock gives the subtle energy system an almighty jolt. When tissues are damaged during an operation or an accident, a simultaneous rupture occurs in the etheric body print. This must be healed along with the tissues to ensure that the damaged area does not remain weak, vulnerable and prone to recurrent problems.

VIBRATIONAL TOXINS

Although we cannot see or feel them, man-made vibrations can have a disruptive influence on the subtle anatomy.

Electromagnetic waves generated by overhead power cables and pylons, televisions, computers, VDUs and radio and satellite transmitters fill the atmosphere with what has aptly been nicknamed as electronic smog. Many artificial waves known as extremely low frequencies or ELFs vibrate in the same range as those emitted naturally. This means they resonate with our own energy waves and encourage them to vibrate at slightly different frequencies that are not natural or conducive to harmony.

Addictive substances such as alcohol, coffee and cigarette smoke are also vibrational toxins.

Alcohol loosens and misaligns the subtle anatomy: the etheric and astral bodies slip out of sympathy with one another, which is how self-control and willpower are weakened. Alcohol also creates a murky, greenish-brown aura congested with a sticky, mucus-like substance.

Cigarette smoke clouds and weakens the subtle anatomy, surrounding it with a fog which dulls the normally vibrant subtle bodies.

Caffeine disturbs the flow of energy in the meridian system. This affects the etheric body, which in turn causes leakage in the emotional and mental bodies. It also upsets the solar plexus chakra, the seat of emotional balance, and the effects filter down to the stomach.

The notion that negative thoughts such as fear, grief, guilt and anxiety are vibrational toxins is mirrored in the shamanic belief that evil spirits act as energy parasites. This may not be as far-fetched as it sounds. It is well-known that brainwaves are electrical waves that vibrate at frequencies between 12 and 0.5 Hz (cycles per second). It is possible that emotions are also wave forms which vibrate at different frequencies, the positive ones being finer and more conducive to harmony than the negative variety.

INHERITED ENERGY FLAWS

Flaws in the energy system known as *miasms* may be inherited. Samuel Hahnemann, the founder of homeopathy, was one of the first modern day physicians to recognize this phenomenon (*see page 81*).

Disease-causing organisms may be cleared by antibiotic therapy but an infection leaves an imprint or flaw in the subtle anatomy which lingers on unless cleared away by an appropriate vibrational remedy. Miasms represent energetic flaws or weaknesses which have the potential to be transmitted back

into the physical body during times of stress, shock and illness.
Because they can be transmitted from generation to generation, miasms are an energetic pathway by which weaknesses resulting from past illness or disease can be passed from parent to offspring.

RESTORING ENERGETIC EQUILIBRIUM

Vibrational healing is based on the notion that the body emits energies or wave forms in a certain frequency range. The harmonious interplay of these frequencies creates patterns or fields of energy that are unique to each person: each individual has their own energetic blueprint.

Vibrational flaws in the energetic blueprint can occur when we are surrounded by frequencies that do not harmonize with our own. These disruptive wave forms range from artificial light waves and electromagnetic waves to the negative thoughts of ourselves and others. Vibrational healing works by flooding the body with frequencies that harmonize with our own, which may come from crystals, music, light, colour, plants and flowers.

A phenomenon known as *resonance* means that when one object or entity vibrating at a particular frequency comes into the proximity of another whose fundamental frequency is in the same waveband, the latter will start to resonate in sympathy with the former. The healing vibrations literally coax our own energetic wave forms into vibrating at the most appropriate frequencies once again. In doing so they restore the true nature of our energetic blueprint. Rather like batteries we can be energized and revitalized when flooded with the right frequencies.

The following chapters explore the natures of these healing vibrations.

SOUND THERAPY

Sound therapy is one of the most ancient forms of vibrational healing. Thousands of years ago Tibetan monks realized that chanting simple sounds could alter states of consciousness and enhance feelings of wellbeing.

Modern sound therapists suggest that illness occurs when energies relating to the mind, body and spirit vibrate at incorrect frequencies. As a result the whole vibrational being goes out of tune. They believe there is a natural note which resonates with each individual as well as with each area of the body. Using specific sound waves or sympathetic vibrations it is possible to restore the correct frequency, resulting in harmony and balance.

Sound can be used in many ways to encourage healing. Most sound therapy involves using the voice, tonal sounds and music, sometimes all three. Some techniques, such as cymatics (*see page 40*) involve using a machine that transmits specific vibrations. From the simple repetition of mystical words to the more complex rhythms and arrangements of notes, sound has the ability to alter our moods and emotions, melt physical tensions, regulate biological processes and raise states of consciousness.

WHAT CONDITIONS CAN BE TREATED WITH SOUND THERAPY?

Sound therapy helps to release deeply buried tensions and traumas which are common causes of much illness. It can help to transform anxiety, depression and low self-esteem into bliss, inner calm and self-worth. By helping to set the mind free, sound therapy promotes clearer thought processes.

As tensions dissolve, niggling ailments such as persistent tiredness, stiff muscles, colds and infections frequently clear. Sound therapy enhances vitality and resilience to all forms of stress and illness.

THE NATURE OF SOUND

Sound is a form of vibration. When you pluck the string of a musical instrument, it causes the air around it to be compressed and then expand. This gives rise to sound waves which travel through space at around 300 metres per second. The rate at which a wave vibrates is known as its frequency and is expressed as Herz (Hz). Different tones are produced by varying frequencies of vibration. The higher the frequency of the tone, the higher its pitch.

Humans have a sonic range (range of hearing) which extends from 20 to 20,000 Hz. Sounds above 20,000 Hz are referred to as ultrasound.

We respond to sound with more than our ears. The entire human energy system responds to the sound waves in our environment.

SURROUNDED BY SOUND

We live in a sea of sound. Our senses are attuned to the sounds around us and we respond to these in different ways. We feel most at ease with naturally occurring sounds such as the rustling of wind through the trees, the babbling of brooks, waves breaking on the shore, the pattering of rain and the rumble of thunder. We are arguably most moved by other people's voices, particularly when they belong to those close to us.

Even before birth we are immersed in sound. A baby nestled inside the womb is soothed by the rhythmic beat of its mother's heart, the gentle rumblings of her digestive system and other bodily processes. Babies become so acclimatized to this background noise that when they are born, they find a world of silence and stillness unsettling. Nothing soothes a newborn baby more than listening to the sound of a beating heart or the steady drone of a Hoover or washing machine.

Babies become familiar with their mother's voice inside the womb and can recognize it after birth. When studying the effect of sound on premature babies, researchers in Paris discovered that a disturbed heartbeat can be restored to a firm, regular, slow rhythm when a mother sings to her baby. Traditional songs of the Hebrides sung by women were the next most effective, then singing from a 12th century Romanesque abbey in Provence. The sound of the ocean also regularized the heartbeat, but when the sound ceased, the heartbeat returned to its original chaotic rhythm.

Nowadays the soothing sounds of nature in our environment are often replaced or drowned out by loud, discordant man-made sounds. In modern urban life we are relentlessly subjected to high levels of background noise – jets, trains, cars and lorries. From the ear-piercing wail of alarms and sirens to the persistent buzzing of the VDU, most artificial sounds grate upon our senses. Constant exposure to loud sounds not only undermines the sensitivity of our hearing, it is also a well-documented source of stress. Sound pollution makes us agitated, irritable and depressed. It can alter the heartbeat and undermine resistance to other ills. There is little doubt that the incidence and level of sound pollution is growing.

To cope with the increasing level of noise in our environment we tend to develop selective hearing. The trouble with shutting down our sense of hearing in order to protect our sanity is that we usually forget to turn it back on again. Over time we may even lose the ability to hear within certain frequency ranges.

VIBRATIONAL PATTERNS

In the 18th century a German physicist called Ernst Chaldni was fascinated by the possibility that sound vibrations can change matter. He scattered sand on steel discs and recorded the way it moved when different notes were played on a violin. The patterns made were beautiful – and reproducible.

Inspired by Chaldni's pioneering work, Dr Hans Jenny of Zurich expanded these experiments using more sophisticated equipment. Jenny poured liquids, plastic shavings, metal filings and powders on discs, then passed different frequencies of vibrations through them. He found that as he went up the musical scale the patterns on the discs altered, and a myriad of shapes were produced which echoed shapes found in nature – the hexagonal cells of honeycomb, the concentric rings of tree trunks, the shapes of snowflakes, starfish and zebra stripes.

Could it be that sound vibrations are the shaping force of nature?

As his work progressed, Jenny was able to transfer notes played into a microphone to a visual form on screen. He found that the Hindu mantra 'om' produced magnificent geometrical shapes.

SYNCHRONIZING SONGS

Ayurvedic medicine uses certain primordial sounds which have a potent effect on the mind, body and spirit. Silently reciting the appropriate sound in the course of a mantra-induced meditation stills the mind and slows the breathing right down. Studies show that such sounds have the power to inhibit the proliferation of cancer cells.

The effects of sound on cell function have been shown in animal and plant studies. Canaries deprived of each other's song experience a retardation in brain growth. In other words, by singing to each other canaries promote and stimulate the development of their brain cells.

Birdsong also affects the health and growth of plants. During the last 15 years, Canadian researchers have been developing an eco-friendly way to boost crop production. It involves playing high frequency electromagnetic waves in a similar range to many bird calls, such as those of swallows, martins and warblers, to the growing plants through a loudspeaker. The sound opens up the stomata – tiny pores on the leaf surface – which allows the plant to absorb nutrients more readily, and the nutrient movement in the plants climbs as much as 700 per cent. Known as Sonic Bloom, the technique is used together with a plant spray containing natural nutrients and hormones and traditional fertilizers such as compost and manure to provide a safer alternative to chemicals.

MIND-BENDING FREQUENCIES

In the last decade sound sequences have been composed with the specific intention of changing brainwave patterns.

The highest frequency waves – beta waves – characterize active thought; the slower alpha waves are associated with meditative states of relaxed awareness. Theta waves are linked to creative insights and may be experienced occasionally as you drift into sleep, which is characterized by the slowest delta waves. Listening to music loaded with certain frequencies can either speed up or slow down the vibrational rate of our brainwaves.

It has been proposed that loading the brain with the frequencies akin to alpha and theta waves may hold the key to instant meditation and creative insight.

Some high frequencies act as natural painkillers. Frequencies in the region of 2,000 Hz are capable of triggering the production of endorphins in the brain, which evoke feelings of bliss, as well as dull the perception of pain.

The high frequency waves emitted by dolphins may explain the uplifting effect many people experience from contact with these creatures.

EMOTIONAL RELEASE

We express ourselves using sound: as well as verbalizing our thoughts and feelings through language, we make a whole range of expressive noises, from moaning, groaning and sighing, to laughing, weeping and crying. These sounds without words portray the full expanse of human emotions including pleasure, pain, joy and sorrow; they are natural, universal and common to all cultures.

In many societies, however, the natural expression of anger, grief and despair through sound is not socially acceptable. Children are frequently told not to cry, yet crying is a way of releasing feelings and preserving good health. Scientists examining the tears of people crying from emotional pain have discovered chemicals in them that differ from those shed while peeling onions. People who cry have fewer stress-related diseases than those who suppress the feelings that trigger tears.

Over the years we can become so accustomed to internalizing our emotions that we find it difficult to express them even when given permission. Even laughter does not always come as easily to adults as it does to children, who giggle at the slightest provocation. Many indigenous cultures recognize that approaching life with humour lightens the mental load. This accounts for the importance of the Heyokah (joker) in Native American traditions and the fool elsewhere in the West. Research shows that laughing stimulates the release of endorphins.

Healers and sound therapists often work by encouraging us to release sounds to express a whole gamut of emotions and so set the healing process in motion.

TONING AND OVERTONING

The sounds of emotions can be produced using various vowel sounds in techniques known as toning and overtoning. These ancient esoteric healing practices can boost energy levels and enhance the joy of life.

TONING

Toning is the vocal release of a vowel sound on a single note. Simple to learn (*see below*) and extremely powerful, the sound alters the vibrations in every cell in the body. After toning,

people find themselves inwardly silent and often unable to speak, as if in a mild trance, feeling at peace and restored. The sound of someone toning reverberates through the atmosphere and affects all those present. The regular practice of toning can release emotional trauma, ease physical discomfort, promote mental clarity and kindle spiritual love.

You can experiment with vowel sounds such as 'eeeee', 'ooooo', 'aaaaa', 'iiiii' amd 'uuuuu', uttering the sound on the out breath and holding it for up to 15 seconds.

Consonants such as 'm' and 'n' are sometimes added to the beginning or end of a tone, or uttered alone. Ancient Hindu mystics used the 'mmmmm' tone which affects the sixth chakra, or third eye, to open and enhance intuition, stimulate the pineal gland and energize the brain.

The call to prayer heard five times a day in Moslem countries combines chanting with toning. Native Americans use similar sounds in their traditional chants and songs.

OVERTONING

Overtones are multidimensional sounds that originate from a single note. When the note C is played on a piano, for instance, the sound we hear is made up of various tones called partial tones. The lowest tone is the fundamental or prime tone and is the loudest of the series. All the other partial tones are upper tones and they vibrate at higher frequencies than the fundamental tone. The first upper or overtone has a frequency twice the rate of the fundamental tone, the second has a frequency three times the rate of the fundamental tone, and so on.

Overtoning or overtone chanting is an ancient shamanic practice that originates in Tibet, Mongolia and southern Siberia. The chanting of Tibetan monks overflows with overtones, as do the haunting Gregorian chants sung by cloistered monks and nuns.

With practice it is possible to sing these overtones. You begin on a single note, but by changing the shape of the mouth and breathing deeply from the diaphragm, you can create higher, bell-like sounds that float above the continuous base note. The songs that emerge sound magical and unearthly.

Overtone chanting evokes a state of complete calm and clarity, which in turn permits greater access to the soul.

SINGING AND CHANTING

Singing of any kind is a wonderful way to release tension, discharge unbearable emotions, lift the spirit and enhance the joy of living. Chanting is one of the oldest singing techniques for instilling a sense of inner peace and clarity. Most chants are religious in origin and were traditionally recited for spiritual purposes. Nowadays, they are perhaps most widely practised to purify, energize and strengthen the mind, body and spirit.

Chanting involves repeating a mantra or piece of sacred text to short phrases of tones, and combining the vibrations of overtones, toning and evocative words to effect mental, emotional and spiritual changes. There are chants designed to enhance meditation, to lift depression, avert danger and express joyfulness.

Chanting is an effective way to release pent-up psychological and physical energy. It can relieve anxiety, reduce fear and obliterate negative vibrations. Those who chant on a regular basis experience greater vitality, clarity of thought, inner calm and joy. Some even report an increase in the sensitivity of their hearing, sight, smell and taste, as well as an improvement in the ability to articulate themselves.

Chanting can cleanse the chakras, and help to restore harmony throughout the body's energy system. A very fine chant was discovered by mystics who lived in Tibetan caves thousands of years ago. They experimented with different sounds until they found separate words for each chakra. Each word was sung nine times, and the note was held for as long as the breath lasts.

Native Americans traditionally see all reality as a subtle web of vibration which can be affected by chanting, prayer and dance. Inspired by the beliefs of his forefathers, Beautiful Painted Arrow of the Ute/Tiwa lineage has built an egg-shaped sound chamber in New Mexico and overseen the construction of others around the world. He describes the chambers as 'our caretakers that help us to access wisdom from an ancient source'. A ceremony is held in the chambers each month during which vowel sounds are chanted to balance various aspects of the physical and non-physical worlds. These vowel sounds are thought to set up a resonance around the world which will affect all reality for the better.

MANTRAS

A mantra is a poetic hymn, prayer, incantation or the uttering of sacred sounds. Mantras are an integral part of every religious or spiritual ceremony. Christian mantras are referred to as hymns. In Hinduism it is believed that the sound approximating to the original 'word' ('In the beginning there was the word, and the word was God'), is 'om'.

SONGS THAT HEAL

Singing whatever notes and words come into your head is also therapeutic. Many sound therapists believe that each person has their own healing song which comforts and helps them to cope with any situation. This song has a basic melody and may have words that do not make sense, like the 'nonsense' songs young children sing, which often contain seed sounds (fragments of words that existed before they were developed into languages).

Many individual healing songs sound like Arabic melodies, Tibetan chants, Native American folk songs or Celtic ballads. Sing your own song silently inside your head until you know it well and can call upon it whenever the need arises.

Remember that any information put into rhythm or music makes a strong impression on the mind, so any words you sing should always be positive, reassuring and uplifting.

SOUND AND THE CHAKRAS

Each chakra is linked to a note. Certain instruments can be used to energize and rebalance the whole chakra system, such as bells or gongs, and crystal bowls are particularly powerful healing tools. Fashioned from pure, clear, crushed quartz crystals into various sizes, a bowl is attuned to each one of the seven chakras. Each bowl, when struck by a rubber gong, emits a note which reverberates through the atmosphere and every cell of the body, clearing disharmony and debris from the related chakra, to enhance the natural resonance of the body.

Crystal bowls have been used in rainmaking ceremonies and to enhance meditative states by activating the vibration of 'om'. They are also incorporated into metaform treatment (*see page 107*).

Chakra	Note
1st (root)	C
2nd (hara)	D
3rd (solar plexus)	E
4th (heart)	F
5th (throat)	G
6th (third eye)	A
7th (crown)	B

CYMATIC THERAPY

Cymatics is the study of how wave forms alter matter. The term was coined by Ernst Chaldini about 300 years ago.

Cymatic therapy was developed by Peter Guy Manners, a British doctor who has been investigating the therapeutic use of sound for around 30 years. Manners proposes that every part of the human anatomy – every molecule in every tissue and organ – emits a sound or vibration of a particular frequency. When the body is healthy, all the molecules vibrate in harmony. When there is illness or dysfunction in an organ or gland, there are measurable changes in its vibratory characteristics.

Manners developed sound patterns that resonated harmoniously with the frequencies emitted by various tissues of the body, which have been scientifically computed. He went on to invent an instrument that can be programmed to emit these harmonies to treat clients. Widely used throughout the world, cymatic therapy can reduce pain and inflammation, whilst increasing mobility. It is particularly beneficial to those with rheumatism, lower back pain, muscle injury, bruising, tendon and joint injury.

The notion that each person has a signature sound that reflects their physical and emotional status has been developed by Sharry Edwards, founder of an experimental new science called bio-acoustics. Her research has shown that certain musical notes may be missing or over-abundant in a person's speaking voice when they are unwell or out of balance. Each person responds to their own individual set of frequencies. When you know your signature sound, you can help your body to heal itself by listening to a tape of your note combined with the frequencies you need.

Man-made electricity and electromagnetic energies seem to be the most influential factors in causing a signature sound to change. Polluted food and water, negative emotions and deleterious environments all have about equal effect, depending upon your particular vulnerabilities.

To date frequency formulas based on signature sounds have helped to treat a wide range of conditions, including insomnia, respiratory problems such as emphysema, heart conditions, high blood pressure, epilepsy, multiple sclerosis, chronic and traumatic pain, broken bones and eye disorders, as well as psychological problems like depression and drug dependency.

INSTRUMENTS OF HEALING

Certain musical instruments emit sounds whose vibrations have a particularly powerful influence on the mind, body and spirit.

With their capacity to conjure up the reassuring beat of the human heart, drums are highly regarded throughout the world. They have been used for over 10,000 years and have evolved into many different forms, from the 18 foot (6 metre)

tall log drums of the New Hebrides and South Pacific, fashioned from hollowed tree trunks, and the enormous barrel shaped dadaikos of Japan, to the small Tibetan damaru, often made from the upper halves of human skulls.

In tribal and nomadic societies of North and Central Asia, the shaman's drum is a tool for transportation between different realities. The shaman drums himself into a trance in which his consciousness is able to travel into and out of the spirit world. Drumming accompanies ritual dances marking important transitions, for instance, to celebrate the cycles of nature, birth, initiation, marriage and death. Such drumming helps to unify the whole tribe and can be a form of mass vibrational healing.

Different rhythms create vibrations which empathize with bodily energy systems. In Japan a special form of drumming is used to stimulate and balance the flow of ki energy through the body.

The Australian digeridoo is another ancient healing instrument. Originally the Aborigines used the digeridoo as an accompaniment to storytelling. When someone was sick it was said that their 'song' had gone wrong and the Aborigines would re-enact their song for them with the help of a digeridoo. The haunting vibrations can clear energy blockages and deeply held physical tensions in the body, which usually result from shock. The treatment is perhaps best described as a kind of vibrational massage.

Simply listening to and passively absorbing different types of music can affect us profoundly. From time immemorial philosophers have believed music has hidden powers.

Pythagoras and the Ancient Egyptians before him discovered a science of vibration which has so far eluded the modern world. By exploring the laws of harmonics, they defined the pattern of resonance between sound and matter. Pythagoras created a table of these ratios known as the Lambdoma Matrix. Whilst generally considered primitive and pre-scientific, this table may hold the key to restructuring matter and healing through sound. The body is a manifestation of a harmonic chord, so the healing music should be replete with the same harmonic intervals. These may be reflected in the ratios of the Lambdoma Matrix.

So what might such music sound like? From antiquity to classical times, the intervals in music were based on the natural laws of harmonics rather than a system of equal intervals between the notes of a scale. The sounds of natural resonance can be heard today in the unadulterated traditional music of India, Iran and Turkey.

SOUNDS THAT STIR THE EMOTIONS

It is well known that certain musical patterns and rhythms have the ability to stir the emotions. At one time or another most people have listened to music that has either moved them to tears or filled them with joy.

Classical composers such as Bach, Beethoven, Vivaldi, Mozart, Handel, Dvorak and Sibelius wrote music capable of taking their audiences on an emotional rollercoaster and enabling them to experience realms of consciousness beyond those of daily life.

In the 1980s, research professor at the New South Wales Conservatorium in Australia, Manfred Clynes (a distinguished Viennese concert pianist and engineer), revealed that emotions correspond to certain melodic structures. Each emotion has a particular form which can be charted by computer graphics. Love, for instance, produces a smooth, deep image, while joy bounces straight up, then floats down again. He defined a Standard Cycle of Emotions, which consists of anger, grief, love, sex, joy and reverence. He suggests that each of these emotions has a span of expression ranging from 4.8 seconds (anger) to 9.8 seconds (reverence).

Clynes also believes that certain passages of music can generate responses such as joy, sadness, love or reverence, depending on the structure of the musical phrases within them.

Music is a powerful tool for controlling mass consciousness as it can affect our behaviour subliminally. Recently an experiment was conducted to discover if the background music played in a supermarket affected the type of wine that people chose to buy. When typical German music was played, two thirds of the buyers opted for German grown wines. When this was replaced by typical French music, two thirds of the buyers brought French wines instead.

RHYTHMS OF LIFE

From a healing viewpoint, notes, chords and harmonies that resonate correctly with us have a positive influence on our health and general wellbeing. Certain tones and rhythms in music affect various bodily functions such as the heartbeat, breathing rate and brainwave patterns. Through a process of entrainment, music with repetitive rhythms coupled with a steady, strong pulsation can synchronize these bodily rhythms with the pulsation.

In the 1980s, the American sound researcher Dr John Diamond studied the effect of rhythm patterns on the body. He found that 90 per cent of people lost up to two thirds of their normal muscle strength when exposed to the short-short-long beat which is typical of much pop music. By contrast he discovered that just the opposite was true of the long-short-short beat characteristic of the Native American tom-tom drum. This rhythm strengthens the body's vitality and muscle power – irrespective of whether or not you actually enjoy listening to the music – which is probably why it was often used in calls to the hunt or war.

Kirlian photography also reveals that sound has an effect on the energy fields surrounding living organisms.

Every chakra is affected by music. Classical symphonies, operas, chorales and concertos work on several chakras during the length of a performance. Hard rock and heavy metal music with its loud, snappy, juxtaposed rhythms and melodies tends to over-stimulate the root (1st), sacral (2nd) and solar (3rd) chakras. In contrast these chakras are soothed by the harmonious sounds of Baroque and chamber music.

Folk music from around the world focuses on the heart (4th) chakra; relaxed reggae music gently coaxes the root (1st) and sacral (2nd) chakras open, while cool 50s style jazz affects on the pineal (6th) and crown (7th) chakras.

Aboriginal drumbeats open up the entire chakra system and take the drummers and listeners into the deep trances of their dreamtime. New age music of all kinds invariably aims to have a restoring and rebalancing influence on all the chakras.

TECHNOLOGICAL USE OF SOUND WAVES

Sound waves that lie beyond our range of hearing are referred to as ultrasonic. Ultrasound has a variety of medical and technological applications. The waves can be used like sonar to illuminate our internal organs and other bodily structures. A classic example is the ultrasound procedure routinely given to pregnant mothers to examine the developing fetus. Ultrasound has brought tremendous advances in surgical procedures, negating the need for cutting and sewing in the removal of cataracts, kidney and gallstones and some tumours. This is because certain high frequency ultrasound waves have the power to break up or explode calcified or diseased tissue.

HOW SOUND CAN BE HARMFUL

Science measures sound in decibels on a scale of 0, which represents total silence, to 140, which is literally deafening. This decibel scale is logarithmic: 100 decibels is not twice as loud as 50, it is 100,000 times as loud. And although the ears compensate for this logarithmic progression, the damage which can be done by high levels of sound is insidious.

Sound is a powerful force and must be used with care. Very loud or penetrating sounds should never be aimed directly at the head or near the ears as they can burst the eardrums causing deafness, and even death. Studies compiled by the National Institute for Occupational Safety and Health in Britain show that prolonged exposure to sounds above 85 decibels can inflict permanent loss of hearing. Short bursts of the same noise can temporarily affect hearing from a distance of five feet (about 2.5 metres).

CASE STUDY

CASE STUDY

Chantal, a 40-year-old teacher and writer, was highly strung and completely overwhelmed by stress. She was living on her nerves and felt extremely restless at night, even though she was exhausted and desperate for sleep. As she found music relaxing, she decided to seek the aid of a sound therapist with a knowledge of signature sounds.

By testing her voice, the therapist found that Chantal was deficient in certain sound frequencies. She was given a variety of sounds to listen to. Those that proved most relaxing were her 'birth note' – the vibrational sound of her time of birth – and the note G sharp. These were provided on a tape which she listened to before going to bed each night. Within a few weeks she was able to unwind enough to sleep, and her nervousness and hyperactivity had disappeared. As a result her energy levels soared and she could manage her stress more constructively.

LIGHT AND COLOUR

The importance of sunlight to health has been recognized for centuries: the Aztecs, Minoans, Ancient Egyptians, Ancient Greeks and Romans all worshipped the sun. The Ancient Egyptians knew how to split sunlight into its component colours and harnessed the healing powers of white and coloured light in their temples at Heliopolis.

As well as promoting feelings of overall wellbeing, sunlight plays a role in regulating many bodily processes. Light therapy evolved from the finding that exposure to sunlight or specific rays in its spectrum can help to relieve a variety of conditions.

THE NATURE OF SUNLIGHT

Sunlight is a form of electromagnetic energy and is composed of a multitude of rays all vibrating at slightly different frequencies.

Modern physics defines a light ray as both a stream of tiny particles and as a wave. The waves are described by their speed, wavelength and frequency (vibrational rate). The higher the wave's frequency, the shorter its wavelength.

The rays in the visible range are violet, indigo, blue, green, yellow, orange and red. When combined, these coloured rays make white light. On either side of the visible spectrum are the warm infrared and the high energy ultraviolet rays. The spectral composition of the sunlight we receive varies according to geographical location and time of day. The ultraviolet portion is greatest when the sun is directly overhead and therefore closest to the Earth. The colour quality of sunlight also changes subtly from dawn to dusk.

Small amounts of potentially lethal ultraviolet light (UV) rays never reach the Earth as they are rebuffed by the protective ozone layer and, along with X rays and cosmic rays, are dissipated in outer space.

The delicate balance of wavelengths in natural sunlight is important for sustaining wellbeing, for throughout the evolution of our species we have become accustomed to and dependent upon this particular mix.

The brightness of sunlight is measured in lux. Typically the intensity of sunlight ranges from 10,000 lux on a cloudy day in northern Europe to 80,000 lux on a sunny day close to the Equator. When compared to indoor lighting which normally lies between 250 and 500 lux, even subdued sunlight is extremely bright.

WHY IS SUNLIGHT ESSENTIAL FOR HEALTH?

Many scientists believe that millions of years ago, light from the sun triggered the chemical reactions that led to the development of life on Earth. Without this light living things would be unable to survive.

We are, however, only just beginning to understand the ways in which sunlight exerts its influence over our entire being.

One of the primal effects of sunlight is to align our patterns of waking and sleeping with periods of light and dark.

Evidence that sunlight influences this sleep/wake cycle is provided by studies which show that in the absence of any environmental stimuli this rhythm would be longer than 24 hours – it would be between 25 and 28 hours.

Both light intensity and the number of daylight hours are important factors in determining how long we feel like staying awake. The light-receptive cells in the eye relay messages about the quality of light to a tiny cone-shaped gland in the brain, called the pineal gland. The pineal gland produces a hormone called melatonin which acts as a natural tranquillizer encouraging us to feel drowsy and unproductive.

In 1980 Professor Alfred Lewy, a research psychiatrist at the National Institute of Mental Health in the USA, discovered that exposure to sunlight suppresses the production of melatonin, encouraging alertness and activity. He found that melatonin levels in the blood were about five times higher during the night than during the day.

If melatonin is nature's sleeping draught, sunlight is her alarm clock.

SUN AND THE ENDOCRINE SYSTEM

Sunlight may encourage seasonal and daily fluctuations in other hormone secretions as well. The pineal gland influences other endocrine glands, such as the reproductive organs. The effect on fertility is most pronounced in animals which is why, for instance, sheep always give birth to lambs in the spring.

Many people notice that their sex drive soars in the spring when the days start to get longer. Studies carried out in Finland have confirmed that conception rates are highest when there are 20 hours of daylight (June and July).

Sunlight also affects the thyroid gland, which produces a hormone called thyroxin, which regulates the overall body metabolism and energy levels. If the thyroid gland becomes sluggish and its hormone output falls you may feel lethargic, sensitive to the cold, gain weight and desire to sleep more. These complaints are all too familiar during the darker months of the year, which may explain why a holiday in the sun energizes and revitalizes us.

ENERGY FROM THE SUN

It is said that in ancient times people were able to see light and its component colours as luminous, swirling lights that flowed into, through and out of everything.

In vibrational healing, sunlight is seen as having a cleansing, refreshing and revitalizing effect on the subtle anatomy.

One of the main functions of the aura surrounding the body is to absorb white light and split it into its component colours. Each subtle body absorbs the ray that corresponds to its own colour. The energy of the rays then flows to different parts of the subtle anatomy and the body to refresh and revitalize them, either by helping the building and repairing process or the elimination and disposal process. In this way the ethereal fluidum helps to transport light energy directly into the cellular structures.

Light energy rays are also drawn in through the chakras, distributed along the spine and then throughout the body's systems. Each chakra absorbs a particular colour frequency from the white light. The energy then flows through the extraordinary and ordinary meridians, organs, blood and nervous system to the cells, cleansing and revitalizing as it goes.

Today most people lead lifestyles that predispose them towards sunlight deprivation. Those who live and work in towns and cities spend the most of the day indoors.

Some suggest that when we are deprived of natural sunlight for a prolonged length of time our health gradually deteriorates. A lack of sunlight may even be implicated in some of the health problems prevalent in modern Western society like heart disease, multiple sclerosis and infertility, as well as depression and other psychiatric disorders.

The effects of sunlight deprivation are particularly pronounced during the winter months when many people find their vitality dwindles and spirits sink. Seasonal Affective Disorder, or SAD, is a form of sunlight deprivation characterized by depression, lethargy, disturbed sleep patterns, a desire to stay in bed, an inability to concentrate, and cravings for carbohydrate-rich foods, especially sugary snacks and chocolate. The best way to alleviate this type of depression is quite simply to get supplementary sunlight (*see page 57*).

People who live in the far north of countries such as Finland and Norway, where the winter nights are almost endless, often sleep for long periods in winter, but hardly at all during the summer. Thus they make fewer demands on their bodies during the darker seasons. In urban society it is normal to toil under electric lights long after the sun sinks below the horizon and to live and work at the same pace all year round. It may be quite natural to feel sleepy and sluggish throughout the afternoon in wintertime when it is dark outside.

ARTIFICIAL LIGHTING – CAN IT REPLACE THE REAL THING?

The invention of artificial lighting enabled us to conquer darkness and acquire a new kind of control over our environment. Nowadays we rely heavily on electric lights to illuminate our lives, but the light they emit does not have the same health benefits as natural sunlight.

The difference between the two begins with the composition of colours. Ordinary incandescent bulbs produce light predominantly from the red end of the spectrum, and have small amounts of blue. Cool white fluorescent lights produce more of the blue and green wavelengths but still do not mimic natural sunlight. Neither emits any ultraviolet light.

Secondly, artificial light, even the fluorescent variety, is dimmer than sunlight. It has an intensity of around 250 to 500 lux; sunlight is at least 10 times brighter.

Research suggests that, when they replace sunlight as a primary source of light, artificial lights with their distorted spectrums disturb the natural equilibrium of the body.

Most life forms thrive on the special mixture of rays present in sunlight with each wavelength playing a particular role in sustaining the balanced functioning of an organism. This was demonstrated back in the 1920s by Dr John Ott, a respected time-lapse photographer who initiated some of the original studies into the effects of different types of light on plants and animals.

While filming a pumpkin flowering for Walt Disney, Ott noticed that pumpkins produced healthy male flowers but withered female ones when grown under ordinary 'warm white' fluorescent light. When cultivated under daylight-mimicking fluorescent light the effect was reversed. The pumpkins grown outdoors in natural light developed both healthy male and female flowers. Ott carried out the same experiment with fish and found a similar effect – they laid either male or female eggs depending on the quality of light to which they were exposed, but equal amounts of both sex eggs in natural sunlight.

Ott's findings led him to conclude that animals kept under full-spectrum sunlight always produced more and healthier young than those exposed to other types of lighting. He even suggested that couples who were having difficulty conceiving should expose themselves as frequently as possible to natural sunlight.

Behavioural problems such as hyperactivity may also be exacerbated by artificial lighting. This phenomenon, also noted by Ott, was later confirmed by research conducted by a lighting company in America. One study was carried out at a school lit almost entirely with fluorescent tubes where hyperactivity was a particular problem. When the lights were replaced with full-spectrum ones there were some notable changes. The children who could hardly stay in their seats before began to sit still and pay attention. The rate of punishment went down, while work output and learning capacity rose.

ULTRAVIOLET
– THE DOUBLED-EDGED RAYS

Of the natural sunlight that reaches the Earth, 50 per cent is visible and 5 per cent ultraviolet (UV) light. Since the discovery that UV rays are responsible for causing sunburn, skin ageing and even skin cancer, this part of the spectrum has been deemed dangerous. In small doses however, UV rays are essential for good health.

It is well known, for instance, that UV light falling on the skin triggers the synthesis of vitamin D in the body. This nutrient is

vital for the absorption of calcium. Although vitamin D can also be obtained through diet (it is found in dairy foods, eggs and fish oils), the sun still seems to be an important factor in sustaining healthy levels of this vitamin.

Not surprisingly, vitamin D levels tend to be markedly higher during the sunnier months of the year. If levels fall too low, symptoms such as bone and joint pain and muscular weakness can set in.

Much research into the effects of UV deficit or 'light hunger' originates from areas of Russia where people are starved of sunlight during long, dark winters. It is commonplace for UV-containing light to be used in schools and factories to improve fitness and reduce infections throughout the winter.

Russian studies suggest that the capacity of white blood cells to combat infections is approximately doubled by appropriate UV light exposure. UV light may also help to control the number of bacteria and viruses in the air we breathe, as it possesses natural germicidal properties.

One Russian study looking at the body's ability to withstand toxic substances and eliminate them from the system concluded that the tolerance of an organism to chemical substances depends to a great extent on its subjection to UV radiation. The ability to detoxify drops when the body has a deficit of UV and increases on exposure to sub-erythemic doses of UV light (less than would provoke sunburn). This suggests that a balanced spectrum containing the correct proportion of UV light helps us to withstand environmental pollutants including pesticide residues, vehicle fumes, and other health-harming chemicals.

Natural sunlight has a tonic effect on the mind, body and spirit. For this reason, it can help to relieve most common ailments.

In general, exposure to sunlight enhances feelings of confidence and self-esteem, encourages relaxation and improves resistance to stress and illness.

Controlled doses of sunlight have been effectively used to treat seasonal depression and weight gain as well as chronic tiredness and lethargy. Light therapy helps to lift flagging libido, enhances fertility, eases arthritic and rheumatic conditions and increases immunity to infections.

SUN THERAPY

Anyone who takes a holiday in the sun is instinctively treating themselves to a dose of sunlight therapy. The Ancient Egyptians and Greeks were aware of the benefits that came from exposing themselves to the sun's rays. At the turn of the century the Austrian naturopath, Bircher Benner (famed for his muesli), recommended exposing the skin to a gentle sun for 30 minutes each day to promote good health. For health purposes it is best to lie in the sun during the early morning (before 10 a.m.) and late afternoon (after 4 p.m.), when the sun's rays are most benign, and contain non-burning amounts of UV rays.

Nowadays some people take sunbathing to an extreme in the pursuit of a tan. Whereas small doses of sunlight are positively beneficial, excessive quantities promote dehydration and do irreparable damage to the skin.

PHOTO THERAPY

Daily doses of light-mimicking full-spectrum daylight are now used for treating seasonal affective disorder or SAD. This therapy emerged during the early 1980s.

Peter S. Mueller, a psychiatrist at the National Institute of Mental Health in the USA, was treating a 29-year-old woman who had suffered from cyclic bouts of depression for several years, during which time she had moved to several different cities. He noted that the further north she lived, the earlier she became depressed in the autumn and the longer she stayed depressed in the spring. On two occasions when she travelled to Jamaica in mid-winter, her melancholy lifted within a couple of days of arrival. Mueller speculated that lack of sunlight contributed to her depression, so on consecutive mornings he exposed her to 2,500 lux of supplemental full-spectrum light. In less than a week her depression had lifted.

Further research shows that exposure to 2,500 lux for two hours in the morning, when the body is most receptive to light stimulus, brings complete relief from both depression and carbohydrate cravings in roughly half those treated, after just a few days.

SYNTONICS

Syntonics was developed by Dr Harry Spitler in the early 1900s and derives from the word syntony, meaning 'to bring into balance'.

Spitler realized that the eyes are directly connected via nerve pathways to portions of the brain responsible for controlling both the autonomic nervous system and the endocrine (hormone) system.

He discovered that light applied through the eyes had a positive influence on the brain's control centre and so, in turn, helped to regulate all the functions of the body. In 1927 he developed the first light-dispensing instrument for ocular application. It feeds the eyes with a beam of light containing the selected portions of the visible spectrum needed to bring the patient's body back into balance. Spitler found that when

nervous and endocrine systems were rebalanced, visual
field, visual attention span and visual memory all improved.

THE HEALING POWER OF COLOUR

Colour is a form of vibrational energy that has played an
important role in health and healing for thousands of years.
The Ancient Egyptians built halls of colour in their great temples at Karnak and Thebes where they researched the influences of light and colour.

Each colour of the spectrum is associated with a range of
wavelengths, which means there are hundreds of subtle
nuances of colour. Not all of these are visible to the human eye,
since colours vibrating at similar rates look very much alike.
Violet wavelengths are the shortest, ranging from around 380
to 450 nanometres (nm). Red wavelengths are the longest,
spanning 630 to 760 nm.

Different colours affect the mind, body and spirit in different
ways, and most cultures associate colours with particular qualities, feelings, and so forth.

Colour is one of the nine basic 'cures' applied in Feng Shui, the
Chinese art of divination and directing energy (qi) to create conditions that are conducive to health, happiness and good fortune.

Each of the Chinese dynasties had a royal colour worked out
by a Feng Shui master – brown for the Sung dynasty, green for
the Ming and yellow for the Ching.

According to traditional Chinese belief, depending on your
date of birth, some colours give you energy, and others take it
away. Different combinations of colour have extraordinary
effects: when some colours are put together they create growth,
while others encourage conflict.

Whilst the symbolism of colours varies between cultures, the
underlying associations tend to be consistent and universal.

WHITE

White is technically not a colour, as it is the result of all the colours mingling together in equal proportions. In the West it is associated with purity, innocence and cleanliness. In China and India it is the traditional colour of mourning.

VIOLET AND INDIGO

These colours are associated with spirituality, loyalty, love and all things divine. Leonardo de Vinci claimed that the power of meditation could be enhanced tenfold under the influence of violet rays passing through the stained glass windows of a quiet church. In muted hues this colour can be helpful for treating headaches, neuroses, and certain forms of schizophrenia and dementia.

BLUE

Blue is associated with faith, caring and fidelity. Cornflower and lavender blue in particular represent spiritualism, thoughtfulness, constancy and kindness.

GREEN

Green is universally considered to be the colour of growth, healing and tranquillity. The green colour of plants promotes peace and harmony for easing troubled minds. Green is associated with the heart and when we think green, it attracts whatever we need to feel nurtured and calm. Too much green can create a static condition because it alleviates all stress.

YELLOW

Yellow represents patience, tolerance, wisdom and mental energy. It helps to expand horizons and brings fulfilment. In China charms against evil spirits are written on yellow paper. The colour has the power of the sun and was once reserved solely for the Emperor.

ORANGE

Orange represents joy, togetherness and feminine sensuality.

PINK

Pink is a warming, soothing, reassuring colour that represents love and romance. When you feel angry, think pink and the anger will evaporate.

RED

Red is a passionate, stirring colour which relates to happiness, life and courage. It is a highly emotional and energizing colour. If you are over-emotional or hyperactive, it is best not to surround yourself with this colour. In China, red is the symbol of virtue.

Science suggests that there is a basis for these associations. Studies have shown that colour can influence mood, perception of temperature and time, and even the ability to concentrate. It is being used increasingly in hospitals, offices, mental health clinics and prisons to create a positive environment.

Red light has been found to speed up the circulation and raise blood pressure, while blue has a calming effect on these processes. The effect is the same even if the patient is blindfolded, which implies that colour does not have to be seen to exert its effects. Blind people can 'see' different colours, so it seems highly likely that we respond to different colour vibrations via the subtle anatomy – the subtle bodies, aura and chakras.

THE LUSCHER COLOUR TEST

In conventional Western medicine the Luscher colour test has been used as a diagnostic tool by psychiatrists and physicians since 1948.

It involves asking patients to arrange coloured cards in order according to the ones they like best. Their instinctive choice reveals a great deal about their state of mind or psyche. Greys and browns suggest holding power meaning a task will be seen through to the end. Orange and yellow indicate happiness and joy, while pink marks a tendency towards self-criticism. Most physicians agree that the test is an early indicator of stress-related problems although they do not entirely understand how the system works. Disorders have been identified long before the physiological symptoms have appeared.

THE SUBTLE ENERGETIC EFFECTS OF COLOUR

In vibrational healing colours are associated with spiritual, emotional, mental and physical qualities. The presence and absence of particular colours in the subtle anatomy provides the healer with information about the person they are treating.

Each chakra resonates with a particular band of colour. The chart opposite shows each colour's connection to the chakras, the qualities associated with it, what its presence means in the subtle bodies and aura, and the health problems associated with its absence.

Colour	Chakra	Associations	Presence	Absence
White	Higher	Cosmos, universal mind	Infinite creative essence	Disharmony of spirit
Shades of:				
White into gold		Essence into form		
Gold		Personal challenge		
Silver		Activation		
Ash		Death		
Violet	Crown	Higher mind	Wisdom, learning, rapid positive change.	Nervous, mental disorders
Indigo	Third eye	Vision, perception	Universal depth, penetration	Eye disorders
Blue:	Throat	Self Expression	Alignment to truth	Disorders of throat, larynx
Shades of blue grey			Mental tension, nervousness, hypersensitivity	
Green	Heart	Inner harmony	Balance of the mind, healing for the body, connection to nature	Heart disease, hypertension
Shades of dark green			Envy	
Yellow	Solar plexus	Intellectual stimulation	Intelligence, health, mental vitality	Stomach, pancreas and liver disorders
Shades of:				
Mustard		Deception		
Sand		Self-deception		
Tan		Concern, worry		
Brown		Practicality		
Chocolate		Evil		
Orange	Hara	Assimilation, circulation	Vitality, concentration of raw energy, power	Lung and kidney disorders
Shades of:				
With brown		Ego		
Brown/orange			Manipulation	
Yellow/orange			Service to mankind, social interaction	

| Red | Root, base | Creativity | Vitality, courage | Anaemia, blood disorders |

Shades of:

Red/Orange	Anger, resistance
Pink	Passion, affection
Deep pink	Love
Rose	Completeness
Hot pink/black	Misuse of sex
Black	Intelligence

Shades of:

Velveteen	Connection to the Akashic records
Sooty black	Negativity
Charcoal	Terror
Soft grey	True intelligence
Dark grey	Avoidance of pain
	Suffering, fear, degrees of darkness

WHAT CAN COLOUR THERAPY TREAT?

Colour therapy can help to treat any disorder but therapists usually emphasize that their therapy is complementary to qualified medical treatment, not an alternative to it. Sufferers from migraine, eczema, asthma, inflammation, rheumatic pain, arthritis, insomnia, stress, high blood pressure, depression and lack of energy have benefited from treatment.

On a more ethereal level, using colour vibrations to restore harmony to the energy systems can encourage healing at the levels of mind and spirit.

HOW A COLOUR THERAPIST WORKS

There are various approaches to healing with colour.

Some colour therapists believe that each vertebra is associated with one of the seven spectral colours as well as being related to a particular organ or part of the body. These colours are repeated in sequence down the vertebrae, increasing in colour density from the neck to the base of the spine. In normal health each vertebra emits energy at a given frequency which the therapist perceives as colour, sound or both. In ill health variations in these patterns occur. By interpreting such changes therapists can recommend a colour prescription based upon a person's individual needs.

As in sound therapy, the appropriate colours or vibrations are applied in ways designed to restore the harmonious function of the whole energy system.

Therapists may feed in the appropriate frequencies by bathing the body in coloured light. They may also work with dyed squares of silk which are held or laid over the patient's body. Colours may be applied alone or in special combinations.

Patients may be asked to shade geometrical shapes with the colours which seem most appropriate to them, as in the Luscher test. Afterwards they draw two pictures using whatever crayons they wish. The colours reveal something about the person's psyche.

Colour therapy can also involve using certain colours in your surroundings. The colours you choose for decoration, clothes, flowers in the garden and so forth all influence your wellbeing. Even coloured foods nourish the system with certain vibrational properties. You can imbibe the positive qualities of orange, for instance, by sipping orange juice, and eating carrots, mangoes and pumpkins.

COLOUR BREATHING

This is a visualization technique which involves imagining breathing in a particular colour. The inhaled colour is mentally directed to areas of illness, blockage and dysfunction, or to those bodily systems that are in need of revitalization. There are variations on this technique which allow the visualized colours to nourish the chakras, subtle bodies and aura.

COLOUR TINCTURES

Liquids infused with colour are another way of applying the healing vibrations.

This particular form of colour therapy has been developed by Vicky Wall into a system known as Aura-Soma. Balance bottles are at the heart of this system. Each bottle relates to a chakra and contains two distinct colours in a plant-derived liquid that is separated into an oily and an aqueous layer. The liquid contains the energies of crystals and gems which reinforce the healing vibrations of each colour.

The appropriate bottle is selected on the basis of the patient's colour preference. In addition to relating to the heart chakra, the blue/green combination, for example, can help to treat a range of ailments affecting the lungs and heart, such as asthma, chronic bronchitis and angina, as well as affairs of the heart. The remedy is applied to the skin which absorbs the healing energies of the essential oils, plant extracts, gems, crystals and colour.

Coloured liquids called pomanders are used for strengthening and enhancing the aura; quintessences act directly on the subtle bodies, encouraging openness to receiving a particular kind of energy that may be helpful in dealing with a certain situation.

Colour can also be imbibed in the form of tinctures relating to the main chakras. They are diluted in water and dropped onto the tongue. They include red, green, yellow, violet, indigo and pink tinctures, and a rainbow tincture to rebalance the whole chakra system.

TRANSMITTING HEALING VIBRATIONS

This form of vibrational healing is based on the notion that people are able to transmit healing energies or vibrations to others.

Healers work in several different ways: by placing their hands on the body, or tapping into key energy points on the body. Some work at the level of the aura and subtle bodies, while others direct healing energy in the form of thought-waves. Many use a combination of these techniques. As with other forms of vibrational healing, the aim is to harmonize and rebalance the body's energy systems.

HANDS-ON HEALING

People have been using their hands to heal since time began. The Ebers Papyrus which dates from around 1552 BC describes the laying-on of hands as a medical treatment.

Four hundred years before the birth of Christ the Greeks used touch therapy in their Asklepian temples. The writer Aristophanes tells us that in Athens, the laying-on of hands was used to restore sight and fertility.

The Bible makes many references to miraculous healing through the laying-on of hands.

Theophrastus Bombastus von Hohenheim, better known as Paracelsus (1493–1541) was one of the earliest proponents of a magnetic vital force of nature. He suggested that the stars and other bodies (especially magnets) influenced humans by means of a subtle fluid pervading all space.

At the time of the French revolution, Franz Anton Mesmer claimed to be able to heal with universal energy which he called fluidum. He defined this as a subtle physical fluid connecting people and other living things, the Earth and heavenly bodies. Like Paracelsus, he thought the vital force was magnetic and referred to it as animal magnetism. Mesmer believed the subtle energetic fluid was somehow associated with the nervous system and carried around the body by the nerves and body fluids. He also suggested that when a person is in good health, he or she is in harmony with nature.

Interestingly, Mesmer's concept of fluidum closely resembles the ancient Chinese model of qi energy which feeds vital force to the nerves and tissues.

Mesmer believed that the energy flow is most active from the palms of the hands, and that placing the hands on another person establishes a direct route for this energy to be transmitted.

More recent laboratory investigations into the physiological effects of the laying-on of hands have confirmed the magnetic nature of these subtle healing energies. It is now widely thought that some people can sense the vibrations a person needs to restore their energetic balance. Many of these healers describe themselves as channels for transmitting 'cosmic' or 'universal' energy containing these vibrations to others.

During a typical treatment a healer lightly touches the patient, instinctively knowing where to place his or her hands. Some say they can actually feel areas of tension or pain in the body.

People receiving hands-on healing have described the healing energy as a tingling, a hot or cool current that flows to certain areas of the body, relieving pain and promoting deep relaxation and overall wellbeing. Miracle cures are rare but some healers channel a particularly potent form of energy and are renowned for their ability to alleviate suffering of all kinds.

THERAPEUTIC TOUCH

This type of hands-on healing has found favour with nurses and healthcare professionals throughout the world, particularly in the United States.

Therapeutic touch was developed in the 1970s by an American nursing professor, Dolores Krieger, after witnessing the work of Hungarian healer Oscar Estabany, and studying with the well-known healer Dora Kuntz.

Those wishing to heal others learn how to focus the mind and cultivate sensitivity. Typically a practitioner runs his or her hands over or near the patient and seeks out areas of disharmony or illness. If anything is found to be wrong the healer places his hands on the area so that the healing energy can flow to the patient. A treatment usually lasts about 10 to 15 minutes, after which the patient should begin to feel better.

Studies have shown that nurses trained in therapeutic touch can produce considerable improvements in the physical and emotional states of their patients.

SUBTLE ENERGETICS OR MICROMOVEMENT

Subtle energetics or micromovement was developed by Herbert Bacia MD who was born in Germany in 1937. Bacia is a medical doctor who worked in hospitals and had his own practice in West Berlin specializing in holistic medicine and homeopathy. While travelling through America, he came in contact with healers whose vision and perception inspired him to formulate his own healing technique. Bacia came to the conclusion that energy flows through the body in the form of rapidly vibrating waves, and referred to this phenomenon as micromovement.

Any kind of emotional or physical trauma disturbs the rhythmic, dance-like motion of these vibrating waves so that they become erratic, stifled, and lose their fluidity. As a result the body loses some of its vitality and flexibility. Postural imbalances may also set in.

The practitioner works by placing his hands on either side of any area of the body, for example by holding the ankles, then moving slowly up the legs. A current of energy flows between the practitioner's hands, amplifying and rebalancing the motion of the energy waves in the patient's body. These effects are achieved by an almost Zen-like approach on behalf of the practitioner, an effortless non-doing.

A deep meditative state of stillness is experienced by the person being treated, which penetrates the whole body. There is a powerful release of tension, a painless opening of any blocked areas. Often deeply buried memories, feelings and insights emerge which are released as the correct subtle energetic movements are re-established.

Subtle energetics is a valuable treatment for all kinds of stress-related disorders, chronic pain and structural imbalances. Sometimes complete pain relief is experienced. Heightened body awareness, improved balance, emotional peace and well-being is often felt during and after the treatment.

CASE STUDY

Angela was 30 years old and had been suffering with painful, blocked sinuses for most of her life. Initial consultation with a subtle energetics practitioner revealed there was much tension at the base of her skull and the whole neck area was in need of realignment. After a series of treatments she experienced deep relaxation and relief. Her sinuses started to clear and she was able to breathe freely for the first time in years.

AURA HEALING

In this form of hands-on treatment the healer works away from the physical body at the level of the aura. Those who practise this kind of healing are usually blessed with an ability to see the aura and can develop this gift by working on their spiritual development. Others can learn to sense its presence and quality with their fingertips.

Past shock and present stresses can leave imprints in the aura. Therapists often refer to these as areas of congestion or 'mucky' energy. In cases of severe trauma the aura may actually break and holes appear. These gaps are potentially dangerous as the physical body is no longer fully protected.

Therapists are channels through which universal healing energy can flow. They visualize the harmonizing vibrations passing through their hands into the other person's aura. Once a therapist has gleaned an image of the aura, he or she rebalances the energetic vibrations in various ways: by visualizing 'feeding' in certain colours, clearing away negative energy, mending holes and generally cleansing the auric field.

Cleansing and strengthening the aura in this way restores harmony and health at all levels.

SPIRITUAL HEALING

Some healers are channels for healing energies of a spiritual nature. This spiritual energy can also be described as cosmic or universal energy, or healing light. Some are born with the ability to heal in this way, but others can learn when they choose to grow and develop spiritually.

Spiritual healers work by channelling energy to others using any of the healing techniques described in this chapter, from the laying on of hands and aura healing to reiki (*see page 78*).

To date spiritual energy has eluded scientific measurement, so no one knows for certain just how spiritual healing works or how far-reaching its effects are. For this reason many are sceptical, and suggest that belief in the abilities of the healer plays an important part in any benefits treatment may bring.

There are, however, several reported cases of infants, unconscious patients, animals and plants responding positively to this kind of healing. The American researcher Dr Dan Benor has published more than 155 controlled studies showing that this form of healing is effective and not just attributable to the power of suggestion.

PSYCHIC HEALING

This is a form of spiritual healing in which the intuitive faculties come into play either through the gift of clairvoyance (the ability to see beyond the norm) or clairaudience (the ability to hear beyond the norm).

A psychic healer may, for instance, be able to sense the condition of the aura, the presence of holes, blockages and negative vibrations emanating from the subtle anatomy and any disharmonious patterns and disease in the organs and tissues.

This talent was attributed to many of the ancient seers and has been maintained by shamans and healers throughout time. Ralph Vaughan (Clare's grandfather) was a renowned Harley Street healer, osteopath and acupuncturist who possessed this psychic ability of x-ray vision. He was much sought after in the 1940s for his accurate diagnostic skills.

This extraordinary aspect of psychic healing came to light in the Philippines in the 1920s and spread through South America in the 1980s, achieving particular prominence in Brazil.

Those who practise psychic surgery are mediums who channel the spirits of outstanding doctors who are deceased, but wish to continue their earthly works from the spirit world.

Psychic surgeons enter into a deep trance while the physician works through them. The physician works with invisible scalpels and other instruments which pass through the patient's body, although they never break the skin or leave any scars.

CASE STUDY

A lady with a heart condition was warned by her doctor, following an X ray examination, that her heart could stop beating at any moment. With nothing to lose she decided to see a famous psychic surgeon called Stephen Turoff who has Dr Khan, an Austrian Jewish doctor, working through him. Doctor Khan worked with her for three consecutive days for a few minutes at a time. She started to feel better and returned to her own doctor for further tests, without mentioning that she had seen Stephen Turoff. Further X rays and scans revealed, much to her doctor's amazement, that her heart was 'as good as new'.

Such cases are rare, as only a handful of those practising psychic surgery possess a genuine gift for this type of healing, and there are many instances of fraudulence.

RADIONICS

Radionics is a form of healing involving distant diagnosis (using psychic skills or intuitive knowledge) in conjunction with a specially designed black box to detect disturbed energy patterns. The practitioner transmits the appropriate healing vibrations from a distance, as well as prescribing vibrational remedies such as homeopathic medicines, flower remedies and colour therapy.

This form of treatment originated in the 1920s when American neurologist Albert Abrams invented a black resistance box which he claimed could pick up a person's vibratory patterns from a 'witness' such as a hair clipping. The black box could also be tuned to transmit the necessary healing energies to that person. This kind of treatment is referred to as 'broadcasting'.

Radionics works on the principle that we are all connected by a vast field of energy surrounding the planet. Patient and practitioner have their own distinct energy fields which can be linked to each other by an act of thought. The radionic instrument simply provides a focus for the practitioner to create a mental and vibrational connection with the patient.

First the patient completes a questionnaire about his medical history. The therapist also asks for a 'witness', such as a drop of blood or snippet of hair, and looks for imbalances or energy blockages in the chakras, congestion in the subtle bodies, and so forth. For example, a high level of toxic residue left over childhood diseases may be found. Through radionics these toxins can be identified and, to some degree, eliminated. During a radionic treatment the practitioner turns the dials on the black box to the radionic rates which recreate the patient's perfect vibrational blueprint. The healing frequencies are directed towards the patient so that they set up a sympathetic resonance with his or her energy system and bring it back into balance.

Radionics aims to improve your overall health and resolve any deep-seated problems in the process. This therapy can be an effective treatment for asthma and eczema, allergies, chronic pain, arthritis and rheumatism, post-surgical pain and discomfort, headaches and migraines, and sleep disorders.

It is non-invasive and completely safe for infants as well
as adults.

TOUCH TECHNIQUES FROM THE EAST

ACUPRESSURE

Acupressure is a primal form of contact healing in China that
has been overshadowed for centuries by its technological suc-
cessor, acupuncture. The practice of using needles to tap into the
body's energy systems probably developed when practitioners
either lost the art of or no longer trusted using touch alone.

In Chinese medicine qi energy flows along meridians, invisible channels which are the energetic equivalent of the nervous
system (*see page 15*). Dotted along the meridians are key points
– acupuncture points – which act as amplifiers, and pass energy from one point to another. You could visualize them as tiny
sparkling lights scattered over the body. Using modern electronic equipment these points have been mapped out on the
skin – they correspond to areas of markedly low electrical
resistance.

By applying gentle finger pressure to key acupuncture
points the acupressurist strengthens the patient's ability to
absorb qi and direct it through the meridians to clear blockages
and stagnation. Some points may feel tender when touched;
these tend to be places where the qi is blocked or congested.

Acupressure is primarily a preventative treatment,
although in the Western world there is a tendency to wait
until physical symptoms have developed before turning to
this form of treatment.

Whilst mainstream acupressure works on the 12 main meridians, a special form of Eastern touch therapy called Shen
Tao taps into the eight extraordinary meridians, which relate
strongly to the mind.

Shen Tao, which translates as 'Path of the Spirit' is particularly effective for clearing the mind of troubling thoughts and inducing feelings of deep relaxation, rather like meditation. The Shen Tao practitioner applies feather-light, barely perceptible pressure to key acupuncture points and may maintain the contact for longer periods of time than an acupressure practitioner.

Before beginning any kind of acupressure treatment, a practitioner uses the typical Chinese diagnostic method of reading the pulses to determine the work that needs to be done. The pulses supply information about the distribution, quality and strength of energy flowing through the meridians. They are located on the radial artery in the wrist – six on the right and six on the left.

Acupressure (and acupuncture) aims to correct energy imbalances, ideally before they have a chance to undermine wellbeing. It can help to alleviate all kinds of health problems including headaches, nausea, travel sickness, digestive problems, hay fever, asthma attacks and sinusitis.

Shen Tao acupressure is a particularly valuable treatment for stress-related problems and for easing emotional upsets.

CASE STUDY

Beth was 40 and experiencing crippling stomach cramps and pains. She was nervous, suffered from insomnia and indigestion, and was unable to keep on any weight. She never sat down to eat, and had multiple allergies. Her doctor suspected she may have stomach ulcers or cancer and recommended exploratory surgery.

Beth looked upon the Shen Tao treatment as a last resort and persuaded her doctor to postpone surgery for four weeks. Her therapist felt her physical problems were an expression of past emotional trauma. Her stomach meridian was weak, suggesting an inability to nurture herself and much nervous anxiety. The bladder/kidney meridian flow was impaired, indicating a difficulty in letting go. Moxa herbs were held near the kidney and stomach acupressure points to warm the digestive system. The weak areas were treated and she was given dietary advice. In just a few weeks her condition improved dramatically. After three months she was symptom-free and had begun to put on weight.

SHIATSU

Shiatsu-style therapies have been practised in Japan for centuries and developed from 'amna', an ancient oriental massage system of rubbing and manipulating the hands and feet. Shiatsu and acupressure were traditionally used as home treatments practised by one member of the family on another, in contrast with acupuncture which developed later.

Despite its long history, shiatsu was not formulated as a comprehensive therapy until early this century. Tokujiro Namikoshi was among the first to popularize the system. Today it is widely practised throughout Japan and regarded as an integral part of a daily regime for health maintenance, rather like working out in the gym.

Like acupressure, shiatsu aims to rebalance the energy flow along the meridians by stimulating or calming key acupuncture points. It is a deep, penetrative kind of massage that can be painful when sensitive points are worked upon.

Most pressure is applied with the pads of the thumbs and fingers, rather than the tips. As the energy flow changes the patient may feel elated or depressed for a time, either during or after the session. Seemingly adverse reactions such as cold symptoms are common and are part of the healing process. They usually clear within a day or two as energy blockages dissolve.

Shiatsu is largely used for preventing health problems by toning up the circulation, lymphatic drainage, the nervous system and the immune system. It can also relieve a wide variety of everyday ailments, especially tension-related conditions such as headaches, migraines and back pain. Shiatsu is also practised as a form of physiotherapy as it increases the general mobility of joints and muscles.

REIKI

The Japanese word reiki, pronounced 'ray kee', is made up of two words: 'rei' meaning spirit, aura or subtle energy, and 'ki' meaning energy or power. Like acupressure and shiatsu, this form of hands-on healing is based on tapping into the invisible energy that permeates all living things.

Reiki is thought to have evolved as a branch of Tibetan Buddhism, and to be hundreds of years old. It disappeared, to emerge again in the late 19th century when the Japanese minister Dr Mikao Usui rediscovered the essence of this healing art.

While studying Buddhism, Usui found information pertaining to the way Buddha healed. Then, during a three week meditation on a mountain top he had a vision of four symbols. Knowledge of these symbols endowed him with the ability to channel healing energy.

Before he died in the 1930s, Dr Usui initiated others into his form of reiki, known as the Usui System of Natural Healing.

One of these reiki teachers was Dr Chujiro Hayashi, who undertook to keep the tradition of reiki alive. He established the first reiki clinic in Tokyo and from then on the popularity of this healing technique grew and spread further afield.

Knowledge of reiki is transferred from teacher to pupil and practitioners acquire the ability to transmit healing energy through a series of initiations.

Learning and practising reiki healing is a process of spiritual and emotional growth. Daily treatment is an excellent form of preventative medicine.

Reiki can be used to heal someone else even when they are not present, for the healing energy can be projected to a distant place.

During a typical treatment the reiki practitioner places his or her hands on certain areas of the body, beginning with the head. Some reiki practitioners do not touch the body, but transmit healing into the aura.

The results of transmitting reiki healing energy to others can be dramatic or gradual, showing themselves in general improvements in health and wellbeing.

QI GONG

This ancient Eastern healing art evolved in China some 10,000 years ago when philosophers believed that before the world was created there was absolute nothingness, from which arose qi. Everything, they proposed, is a manifestation of this qi which pervades everything and is the very nature of the universe.

We share this subtle energy with the universe. When we are born, our qi is balanced and in harmony with the universal qi. We are pure and fluid, calm, relaxed and carefree, but as we go through life our qi becomes blocked.

The word qi combined with gong translates as 'the subtle energy that flows and feels like the air'. Gong also means 'accumulated time', suggesting that the more time you spend practising, the higher the levels of calm and spirituality that can be achieved.

Taoist masters, Confucians and Buddhist monks all practise Qi Gong for it is the path to perfection, physical transformation

and spiritual enlightenment. It also forms the foundation of martial arts training.

Qi Gong is a very subtle form of exercise in which a person performs slow movements, similar to those of T'ai Chi, to balance the flow of their qi energy. Regular practice clears blockages, so the energy balance within is in harmony with the universal qi. Health improves, healing abilities often develop and the eyes are opened to different realities.

Qi Gong masters can perform healing, as they are able to enhance and direct the flow of qi within a person's body, often working at a distance of several feet from the patient. This technique has been known to cure stubborn illnesses such as diabetes, high blood pressure, arthritis, ulcers, heart disease and migraines.

Qi Gong is a widely accepted healing therapy in China, where there are Qi Gong clinics in many hospitals.

VIBRATIONAL MEDICINES

Vibrational medicines are taken internally, like vitamins and minerals, to restore energetic equilibrium. They can be used alone, or in conjunction with other vibrational therapies to enhance their influence on the body's energy systems.

HOMEOPATHY

Samuel Hahnemann (1755–1843), the founder of homeopathy, proposed that we are all endowed with vital force or life-giving energy. In order to survive and thrive we need to find a way of existing in harmony with our natural environment, a phenomenon biologists refer to as *homeostasis*. Homeopaths believe the vital force continually adjusts throughout our lives to keep us healthy and balanced. The symptoms of illness are signs that the body is coping with some kind of stress.

Homeopathic remedies work by stimulating the vital force, helping the body to deal with the stress and return to a state of equilibrium. A homeopath chooses a remedy that is the best match for a particular profile of symptoms.

The basic principle of homeopathy is 'similia similibus curentur' or 'let like be cured with like' which suggests that any substance that makes you unwell can also cure you.

Hahnemann was inspired to formulate his system of medicine after discovering that a herbal remedy for malaria, the cinchona tree bark, actually produced the symptoms of the disease when taken by a healthy person. He also noted that the more a remedy was diluted, the more effective a cure it became. Homeopathic remedies contain such infinitesimal quantities of the original substance that sceptics find it difficult to believe they can have any effect whatsoever. Paradoxically the more a remedy is diluted and successed (vigorously shaken), the stronger a cure it becomes. A 6x dilution is called a low potency and a 200x dilution is a high potency.

He then proceeded to establish the symptoms produced by a wide range of natural substances in a process called proving. These are listed in the *Materia Medica*.

Some homeopaths also believe the remedies contain the energy essence of the plant or substance from which they were prepared, which has a particular frequency. A skilled homeopathic practitioner will match the frequency of the homeopathic medicine to the energetic frequency needs of the patient.

The correct homeopathic remedy not only alleviates the symptoms but also enhances the life force so that mind and body function harmoniously once again.

Certain homeopathic remedies called constitutional remedies strengthen the body's natural resilience to illness and improve general health, by clearing away the residual effects of any illness or past trauma and enhancing life force.

Homeopaths define a person's constitution as their temperament and state of health. It is your genetic inheritance modified by experiences in life and the environment. Whilst someone with a strong constitution can withstand a considerable amount of stress without falling ill, someone with a weaker one will be more susceptible to all kinds of health problems.

In the early days of practising homeopathy Hahnemann was bemused by the fact that some patients failed to respond to their constitutional remedies and others improved, only to relapse again after a short time. Eventually he discovered a common thread running through all these difficult cases: certain diseases were present in their personal or family history which prevented the constitutional remedy from working properly – the energetic imprint had been left behind. Hahnemann called the blocks 'miasms' and defined three basic ones which he believed to be the underlying causes of chronic disease. One example is the tuberculosis miasm which is associated with a susceptibility to respiratory, circulatory, urinary and digestive disorders. More recently other miasms have been identified, including petrochemical, radiation and heavy metal miasms.

CRYSTALS AND GEMS

Many healers use crystals, gemstones and minerals to provide the vibrations a person needs to realign their energy systems. Because of their special geometric form, crystals can tap into energy patterns that science is only just beginning to discover.

In ancient times various precious and semi-precious stones were held in high esteem along with metals such as gold and silver. It can be argued that these natural elements were originally valued primarily for their ability to heal and preserve feelings of wellbeing. Originally, jewellery may have been seen as a means of protecting and enhancing the body's energy field. Certain esteemed gemstones and crystals were set in crowns, necklaces and belts to position them over key chakras. Native American healers, the Aborigines of Australia and the Jivaro of South America all regard quartz as the strongest crystal of all.

QUARTZ CRYSTALS

There are many members of the quartz family, including amethyst, smoky quartz, citrine or golden quartz, rose quartz and rutilated or tourmalinic quartz – each of which has its own subtle energy and healing properties. The variations are due to the presence of various trace elements. All quartz crystals, however, are fundamentally composed of silicon dioxide.

Science and the esoteric arts alike value the crystals for their ability to amplify, focus, transform and store different kinds of energy.

Quartz crystals are generally thought to amplify and purify the subtle energies. They absorb negative energies and transmit only frequencies of a positive, beneficial nature when programmed to do so (*see page 87*). For this reason they are primarily used to enhance and cleanse a person's energy field.

Quartz crystals are silica-based and have a very stable energy, a very precise and regular vibration. Humans, on the other hand, are carbon-based and inherently unstable.

Quartz crystals owe their special properties to their unique structure. All crystalline structures have a mathematically precise and orderly lattice arrangement of atoms. This immaculate structure responds to a wide spectrum of energies such as light, sound, heat, bio-electricity and even waves of consciousness (thought waves). When such energies are directed at a quartz crystal, its molecular structure oscillates to generate specific vibratory frequencies.

Quartz crystals are the central components in watches and other precise time-keepers because their oscillations are so regular that time can be measured by them.

Crystals are now being used to transmit healing in ways, as legend has it, that were employed thousands of years ago in Atlantis and other mythical civilizations.

Crystals are increasingly being used for communication and to enhance the potency of healing vibrations. As energy passes through a crystal, it is amplified, focused and directed to the areas of the body most in need of rebalancing.

The healer may hold the quartz crystal in his or her hand, or place crystals and gemstones on and around the person. This sets up a powerful energy field which encourages the person's own subtle energies to vibrate at finer frequencies and to clear away static and negative energies. Quartz crystals are useful for rebalancing and cleansing abnormally functioning or blocked chakras. The appropriate crystal or gemstone is placed over the chakra and energy directed through it from the healer.

A healer can charge a crystal with a pattern of energy (or thought wave). The crystal is given to the patient to hold. Even in the healer's absence the crystal discharges its stored healing energies. Alternatively, a healer may hold a crystal and imagine sending the energy to an absent patient in need of healing. The crystal amplifies the thought wave of healing intention and broadcasts it to the patient.

CLEANSING

A crystal used for healing must be cleansed of old vibrational energies so it will carry out its functions clearly. Since crystals can be programmed with negative intentions, this is particularly important. (It is also a good idea to buy from a supplier you either know or have been personally recommended.) Most crystals should be cleansed occasionally so they maintain their potency.

There are many ways to cleanse crystals of undesirable energies:

- Take the crystal to the sea and let the sea water wash over it, then leave it in the sun to be potentized by the sun's energy. Alternatively, soak the crystal in salt water.
- Place the crystal in a spring, river or lake, or let ordinary tap water run over it, then potentize it in the sun. Water is the universal cleanser.
- Soak the crystal in water containing rose or apple blossoms for 24 hours. The essence clears away any stored negativity and the flowers' purity is transmitted to the crystal.
- Adding two drops of pennyroyal, yarrow and sweet grass flower essences to a bowl of water also makes an excellent crystal cleanser.
- Native American and African peoples traditionally cleanse crystals by smudging them with the smoke of sage, cedar and sweet grass burnt together.
- Place crystals in the light of a full moon to endow them with a soft, fresh quality.

Crystals can be awakened by sounding a Tibetan bell, a gong or crystal bowl, which activates their resonant qualities.

CHARGING

Crystals can be charged by placing them in direct sun or moonlight on days of the equinox when the universal energies are particularly potent.

PROGRAMMING

A crystal can be programmed for a task such as healing, meditation or dowsing by projecting a thought or intention at them. This kind of instruction should always be of the highest and purest nature, such as 'for peace and understanding'. Crystals are like computer floppy discs in their ability to accept and store energetic information. They should, however, only be programmed to accomplish one purpose at a time.

RECORD KEEPER
CRYSTALS AND CRYSTAL SKULLS

Legend has it that crystals exist which hold the secrets of the universe. The Atlanteans and Lemurians reputedly perfected the art of programming crystals to the point that they could use them as teaching tools and libraries.

The record keeper crystals can be recognized by one or more perfectly formed pyramids, on one or more of the crystal faces. These pyramids are reputedly the doorways to the records. It is said that the crystals were programmed with ancient secrets such as the origins of the human race and soul. Some were hidden away for future generations to find, and others were lost.

In the 1920s a life-size quartz crystal skull carved in a perfect likeness of a human skull was found in the ruins of an ancient Mayan temple in the Hondurian jungle. More have been found

88

since. They appear to have been used in Mayan and Aztec rituals for their miraculous healing properties. Modern day South American shamans speak of a circle of skulls programmed in Lemuria and Atlantis by the elders, each holding secret knowledge of the universe. When the time is right, their memory programmes will be accessed and the knowledge will be available to benefit all mankind.

WARNING

Crystals can be programmed with harmful as well as beneficial energies, so it is important for crystals to be dedicated for good. There are no other contraindications to crystal healing, although only reputable practitioners should treat babies, children and pregnant women.

CRYSTAL ESSENCES

Crystals can also be taken internally in the form of essences which capture and convey their energetic qualities. These vibrational remedies offer a cheaper means of reaping the benefits of the expensive gemstones such as diamonds, rubies and sapphires. The ancients referred to quartz crystal as 'frozen water from heaven' or 'solidified light'. When the energies of quartz crystals are imbibed, they encourage us to vibrate at a finer frequency by clearing static energy and making all the cell membranes more permeable. In this way they make communication easier and raise our levels of awareness.

Biologists now understand that many substances and membranes within the human body function in the same way as liquid crystals.

A crystal essence sets up a resonance with the crystalline structures of the body and because each crystal holds within its structure a matrix of perfect balance, when ingested the liquid

crystal is magnetized towards the area of imbalance.

Liquid crystals are regarded by many healers as catalysts for change. They form a supportive foundation for the more ethereal frequencies of flower essences and help to anchor spiritual forces into the body. Quartz crystal elixirs are excellent for enhancing meditative states.

GEMS AND THEIR REMEDIES

Gemstones, jewels and precious metals have always entranced mankind. For centuries certain stones have been considered auspicious and in legends they are connected to astrology, healing, magic and spiritual practices.

Kings, popes and other religious leaders used to wear jewels such as diamonds, rubies, sapphires and emeralds to enhance their personal power.

In many cultures crystals and gemstones are assigned to a particular day of the week, and a planet in the heavens. This suggests that certain crystals are particularly potent on certain days and when the planets are in an auspicious alignment. Interestingly, beliefs about the qualities of the gemstones vary very little from civilization to civilization. Rubies, for example, are associated with courage and used for healing blood-related problems such as circulatory disorders, anaemia, ammenhorrea, low blood pressure and irregular heartbeat. Emeralds help to improve eyesight, and pearls, associated with the moon, are helpful in the treatment of asthma, menopausal problems and inflammation. Topaz is a centring stone that can restore sleep and restfulness.

Gems are considered to have a clearer, more powerful energy than crystals, having more stable inherent medicinal properties. Like crystal essences, gem remedies interact with

the crystalline structures of the body. When ingested, the energy imprint in the water is transferred directly to a person's subtle energy system in the same manner as crystal essences.

Some crystals and gemstones have a particular affinity for certain chakras or subtle energy bodies. In crystal and gem therapy a healer places the stones directly over the related chakras and areas of the body. When ingested, the essences gravitate towards the specific chakra or subtle body with which they resonate. In their mode of action, gem remedies lie between homeopathic remedies and flower essences, resonating more closely with the physical body, then moving out to more subtle and spiritual dimensions.

In Tibet and India gems have been crushed to a fine powder and made up into pills and balms for centuries. Gems are commonly used in homeopathic clinics throughout India. A colour is often ascribed to each gem remedy which does not necessarily coincide with the colour of the gem. The given colour is used to guide the doctor when prescribing gem remedies. The doctor checks for 'colour hunger' by using a prism or pendulum to see whether a patient is lacking a particular colour. If he or she is deficient in orange and indigo, for example, pearl and diamond remedies will be given.

HOW CRYSTAL ESSENCES AND GEM REMEDIES ARE MADE

These subtle energetic liquids can be prepared in various ways but most commonly they are made by soaking the chosen crystal, gemstone or mineral in spring water and exposing them to sunlight to extract the vibrational frequencies. The water holds the memory of the vibratory imprint of each stone.

Another method involves placing the stones in phials of alcohol for prolonged periods of time, usually in a dark container, until all the vibrations or frequencies of the gem have been absorbed into the liquid. Crystal essences and gem remedies can be blended with flower remedies, sea and environmental essences in mixtures specially tailored to suit the individual.

THE PROPERTIES OF CRYSTALS AND GEMS

Crystal/gem	Chakra	Influence on subtle anatomy
Amber	Crown, solar plexus, hara	Mental body; transmutes negative to positive energy
Amethyst	Crown, third eye	Mental, emotional and spiritual body
Diamond	All	Cleanses all subtle bodies, aligns the etheric and the physical, draws out negative energy
Gold	Heart, solar plexus, crown	Emotional body, attracts positive energy into the aura
Jade	All	Astral, causal, spiritual bodies
Lapis lazuli	Third eye, throat	Cleanses etheric, mental and spiritual bodies
Moonstone	Heart, solar plexus	Emotional and astral bodies
Quartz	All	Etheric and emotional bodies – dispels negativity

Spiritual properties	Uses
Transforms spiritual desires into reality, unconditional love, spiritualizes intellect	For problems relating to thyroid, nervous system and brain; calms nerves and viral inflammation
Spiritualizes meditation	Boosts metabolism, immune and endocrine systems; for problems relating to brain and nervous system, e.g. migraine and mental imbalances
King of crystals, master healer; enhances spiritual unity and purity	Adjusts cranial plates; for brain imbalance and disease
Dream crystal for inner vision; amplifies and stores thoughts and information, releases past life knowledge	Reduces stress and balances personality; universal healer
Mayan dreamstone for dream solving, access to spiritual worlds and spiritual learning; promotes wisdom	Balances spleen, circulation and kidneys; for female fertility and eye disorders
Soul stone promoting deep soul experiences and total awareness; promotes mental clarity and strength; releases tension	Stimulates thymus and lymphatic system; for tonsillitis, bronchitis and Hodgkin's disease
Lunar stone; for new beginnings, understanding your destiny, enhances intuition	For pregnancy, childbirth, fertility problems and menopause, emotional stress, insomnia, digestive and intestinal problems such as ulcers and oedema
Receives, stores and transmits energy, amplifies thought forms; for affirmation and programming work, meditation and intercommunication	For fevers, blood problems and kidney disease

PRINCIPLES OF VIBRATIONAL HEALING

Crystal/gem	Chakra	Influence on subtle anatomy
Rose quartz	Heart	Emotional, astral, mental bodies
Silver	All	Astral and etheric bodies
Turquoise	All	All subtle bodies, strengthens meridians

FLOWER ESSENCES

Around 10,000 years ago the Australian Aborigines were using remedies made from flowers to ease emotional upsets and achieve peace of mind. The Native Americans, Minoans, Ancient Egyptians, and medicine men throughout the world have also harnessed the healing powers of flowers

For many years the practice was forgotten in the West. In the 1920s Dr Edward Bach, a respected Harley Street physician specializing in pathology and bacteriology, rediscovered this lost art.

Bach was disenchanted with the medicinal approach to treating illness which focused almost exclusively on relieving symptoms, rather than treating the underlying causes. He realized that emotions and states of mind have a powerful influence over physical health. Bach began a quest for a new system of healing that could help with the psychological aspect of illness and found it in the flowers blossoming in fields and hedgerows of the British countryside.

Spiritual properties	Uses
Stone of love, receptivity, attunement to spiritual love; heals childhood wounds; for confidence and creativity	For problems of the heart, circulation, kidneys, male fertility
Soul mirror: encourages awareness of purpose, enhances powers of the moon and feminine qualities	Helps balance right and left brain, enhances IQ; for autism, dyslexia, epilepsy, coordination, visual problems
Master healer: for spiritual attunement and protection from negativity and radiation	For clearing congestion and mucus; anorexia, bulimia; enhances tissue regeneration, absorption of nutrient

The first remedies Bach sought out related to what he saw as the 12 key personality types. The next 26 flower remedies were for bringing relief from different kinds of emotional discomfort. For many years Bach's 38 flower remedies stood alone.

Recognizing the need to find ways of dealing with increasing varieties of stress, many people throughout the world have investigated the healing qualities of other flowers. In the mid–1970s Richard Katz established the Flower Essence Society in California. His aim was to research new flower essences and gather together those working with the essences to exchange ideas and information. The Flower Essence Society now provides over 100 essences from different flowers which are used in more than 50 countries.

The new flower essences are made from an extraordinarily diverse variety of flora, ranging from hedgerow and alpine flowers to exotic orchids, antique roses and the blossoms of fruits such as avocado and banana. Some flowers, especially

those indigenous to the Australian bush, Himalayan mountains and Hawaii, have a long tradition of being used in natural medicine.

HOW FLOWER ESSENCES HEAL

These subtle elixirs help to rekindle a feeling of wellbeing in mind, body and spirit. While some bring relief from unsettling moods and emotions such as anxiety, fear, guilt and anger, others encourage us to recognize and let go of deep-seated behavioural patterns that give rise to such negative feelings. Above all, they help us to feel calm and content in times of stress, and can play an important role in helping us through major transitions in life.

The healing power of flowers resides in their special energetic or vibrational qualities. The energy of every flower is unique and has its own characteristics. Native peoples have always considered plants as living beings whose energy or life force is most concentrated in their flowers. We may not be able to see or touch these energy fields but many sensitive people can feel their strength and quality. These people use a method called Devic Analysis to attune themselves to the flowers, and glean knowledge of their energetic quality and healing potency.

Flower essences act as catalysts for bringing our energies back into balance. They are able to do this because they emit vibrations at frequencies close to those of our own subtle energies. Flower remedies work to realign and pull the subtle anatomy back into order so the self-healing process can begin. They act in a very specific way, travelling to the area most in need of attention.

Areas where vibrational imbalance exists literally soak up the essence's healing energy. Rebalancing occurs as toxicity, in the form of disharmonious frequencies, is flushed from the system. Flower remedies have a particular affinity for the chakras and subtle bodies, although some directly influence the physical body.

Some flower remedies act primarily at the emotional and mental levels, while many of the newer essences made from roses, orchids, lotus and other exotic blooms act at a higher, more spiritual level.

CAPTURING THE FLOWER'S ENERGIES

Bach captured a flower's healing essence by floating freshly picked blooms in bowls of spring water and leaving them in the sunlight on a cloudless day. He then mixed the potentized water with brandy, which is a preservative. Most flower essences are made in this way. Unlike many aromatherapy oils and herbal medicines, these remedies do not contain chemical substances.

Flower essences can also be made by covering newly picked flowers and stems with spring water and bringing them to the boil, uncovered. After simmering for 30 minutes the liquid is left to cool; when cold, the essence is filtered. Again, this liquid is bottled half and half with brandy.

Flowers for healing should be growing wild, in places that are not often visited and are free from pollution. If they are cultivated, it is important that they are tended with loving care and without chemical pesticides or fertilizers. Conscious that the increasing demand for some of the rare flowers may jeopardize their existence, many are turning to alternatives. In India, Dr Atul and Rupa Shah have devised a technique which means they do not have to cut the flowers to make the Aditi Flower Essences. Andreas Korte has invented a crystal method which he uses to make his Amazonian orchid and rose essences.

USING FLOWER ESSENCES

The beauty of flower essences is that you can prescribe them for yourself and others. Simply choose the essence whose qualities best describe your particular problem, for example mood swings, poor immunity, or a spiritual predicament such as 'What is my purpose in life?' It is best to be as specific as possible, using just two or three essences at a time.

The combination of flower essences should match your energetic blueprint. This sets up a sympathetic resonance so that your body can be reminded of how it really should be. It is like sounding a chord that brings all the notes into perfect harmony.

Reproduced by kind permission of Julian Barnard.

In these brief descriptions the negative state is given first with some positive aspects at the end in *italics*. The full description for each remedy state, as given by Dr Bach, can be found in *The Twelve Healers and Other Remedies* (Society of Metaphysicians, 1996).

Agrimony: worry hidden by a carefree mask, apparently jovial but suffering; *steadfast pace.*

Aspen: vague, unknown, haunting apprehension and premonitions; *trusting the unknown.*

Beech: intolerant, critical, fussy; *seeing more good in the world.*

Centuary: kind, quiet, gentle, anxious to serve, weak, dominated; *an active and positive worker.*

Cerato: distrust of self and intuition, easily led and misguided; *confidently seek individuality.*

Cherry plum: for the thought of losing control, of doing dreaded things; *calmness and sanity.*

Chestnut Bud: failing to learn from life, repeating mistakes, lack of observation; *learning from experience.*

Chicory: demanding, self-pity, self-love, possessive, hurt and tearful; *love and care that gives freely to others.*

Clematis: dreamers, drowsy, absent-minded; *brings down to earth.*

Crab Apple: feeling unclean, self-disgust, small things out of proportion; *the cleansing remedy*.

Elm: capable people, with responsibility, who falter, temporarily overwhelmed; *the strength to perform duty*.

Five Flower Remedy: the rescue remedy combination of Dr Bach: Cherry Plum, Clematis, Impatiens, Star of Bethlehem and Rock Rose. For use in any sudden difficulty.

Gentian: discouragement, doubt, despondency; *take heart and have faith*.

Gorse: no hope, accepting the difficulty, pointless to try; *take heart and have faith*.

Heather: longing for company, talkative, overconcern with self; *tranquillity and kinship with all life*.

Holly: jealousy, envy, revenge, anger, suspicion; *the conquest of all will be through love*.

Honeysuckle: living in memories; *involved in present*.

Hornbeam: feels weary and thinks can't cope; *strengthens and supports*.

Impatiens: irritated by constraints, quick, tense, impatient; *gentle and forgiving*.

Larch: expect failure, lack confidence and will to succeed; *self-confident, try anything*.

Mimulus: fright of specific, known things – animals, heights, pain, etc., nervous, shy people; *bravery*.

Mustard: gloom suddenly clouds us, for no apparent reason; *clarity*.

Oak: persevering, despite difficulties, strong, patient, never giving in; *admitting to limitation*.

Olive: exhausted, no more strength, need physical and mental renewal; *rested and supported*.

Pine: self-critical, self-reproach, assuming blame, apologetic; *relieves a sense of guilt*.

Red Chestnut: worry for others, anticipating misfortune, pro-jecting worry; *trusting to life*.

Rockwater: self-denial, stricture, rigidity, purist; *broad outlook, understanding*.

Rose rock: feeling alarmed, intensely scared, horror, dread; *the courage to face an emergency*

Scleranthus: cannot resolve two choices, indecision, alternat-ing; *balance and determination*.

Star of Bethlehem: for consolation and comfort in grief, after a fright, or sudden alarm.

Sweet Chestnut: unendurable desolation; *a light shining in the darkness*.

Vervain: insistent, wilful, fervent, enthusiastic, stressed; *quiet and tranquillity*.

Vine: dominating, tyrant, bully, demands obedience; *loving leader and teacher, setting all at liberty*.

Walnut: protection from outside influence, for change and the stages of development; *the link breaker*.

Water Violet: withdrawn, aloof, proud, self-reliant, quiet grief; *peaceful and calm, wise in service*.

White Chestnut: unresolved, circling thoughts; *a calm, clear mind*.

Wild Oat: lack of direction, unfulfilled, drifting; *becoming definite and purposeful*.

Wild Rose: lack of interest, resignation, no love or point in life; *spirit of joy and adventure*.

Willow: dissatisfied, bitter, resentful, life is unfair, unjust; *uncomplaining, acceptance*.

CASE STUDY

Mary had been married for eight years and although she was now three months pregnant, she had experienced problems both conceiving and carrying a baby to full term. She had miscarried four years previously, had polyps removed from her uterus, then suffered another miscarriage two years later.

She was very anxious about losing her baby and her highly stressful job only made matters worse.

Mary was prescribed a mix of flower remedies including Star of Bethlehem (Bach) for past long, slow shock, and pomegranate

(Flower Essence Society) to stabilize the baby and whole reproductive area. Crystal rescue remedy was added to boost self-
healing and buffer both mother and baby from any future
stress or shock.

This combination was taken as a four month course of treatment. Mary had a trouble-free pregnancy and at nine months
gave birth to a healthy, happy baby.

SEA ESSENCES

These are remedies which capture the energetic qualities of the
ocean. Covering three quarters of the entire surface of the
Earth, the ocean is composed of a salty solution which closely
resembles the composition of our own body fluids. In mythology and traditional Chinese medicine, water symbolizes the
emotions, the subconscious realms, growth and maturity.

Any contact with the ocean brings an awareness of its powerful tranformational qualities. The sea can swing from one
extreme to another, from a state of tranquillity to raging tur-
bulence. It is possible to tap into these qualities by utilizing
the energy of organisms that live and thrive in this enigmatic
environment.

These essences are made by placing organisms such as pink
seaweed, starfish, anemones and surfgrass in salt water in either
a crystal bowl or geode, and potentizing it in the sunlight.

Sea essences are dynamic, quick acting and work with the
rhythm and movement of life and the universe. They are for
transformation, transition and change, and major break-
throughs in consciousness. They challenge us to let go or to 'go
with the flow'.

POTENTIZED OR
ENVIRONMENTAL ESSENCES

We are profoundly affected by the environment we live in. It sustains us, providing us with both the physical and energetic nourishment we need to maintain our lives at all levels. At the most basic level, we share the same elemental composition as our natural environment and are constantly interchanging energy and substances with it – for instance, trees and plants cleanse and recycle the air we breathe.

Environmental essences are made with this co-existence in mind. The process begins with identifying the specific qualities in the environment that are needed for healing. A form of conscious and focused attunement with forces of nature occurs and the energies present are transferred into a bowl of water that has been prepared. The natural energies may have been collected during a solstice thunderstorm, under the swirling multi-coloured lights of the aurora borealis, or water from a rainbow glacier high up in the Alaskan mountains.

These are totally unique essences designed to stimulate and support change and transformation. They act as catalysts for deep, strong cleansing, which makes them particularly useful for those living in cities where contact with nature and the elemental forces is weak. They provide stability and support during natural disasters such as earthquakes and hurricanes, when nature herself is in major transition.

VIBRATIONAL HEALING IN ACTION

CHOOSING THE BEST TREATMENT FOR YOU

Vibrational healing views each person as an individual endowed with their own unique pattern of vibrations. The basis of any vibrational therapy is to discover the nature and site of any energetic imbalance and then to feed in the vibrations that are needed to re-establish a state of balance. It therefore makes sense to seek out the form of vibrational healing that you are instinctively drawn towards and feel comfortable with, as the energies involved are most likely to resonate with your own energy field.

Does music move you to tears or fill you with joy? If so, you may enjoy and respond well to sound therapy. Are you artistic, do you have a good sense of colour and are you naturally drawn to certain shades? Then you may find colour therapy helpful. If you are a warm, physical person who is soothed and comforted by touch, you may find hands-on treatment such as subtle energetics or acupressure particularly nurturing. Those who fill their rooms with flowers, enjoy gardening and find solace simply being in nature may feel an empathy for the flower remedies.

When choosing the best vibrational therapy for you, it is important to follow your instinctive urges rather than to listen to the accounts of others. What benefits one person does not necessarily influence another in the same way.

CHOOSING THE RIGHT PRACTITIONER

It is fundamental to find a practitioner with whom you feel a positive empathy. Ideally your practitioner should be affiliated with a recognized body of vibrational healers (*see Resources, page 109*) and will have undergone various training courses, but a natural gift for healing ranks as highly as any formal qualification.

Those dedicated to practising vibrational healing are constantly striving to ensure that their own energy field is clear, vibrant and well-balanced. In other words, they practise what they preach. Such people will be sensitive to the needs of others and often show an intuitive understanding of your problems. They should be able to sense the nature of your energy field and know which frequencies are required to bring it back into balance. Some truly gifted healers may even be clairvoyant.

It is said that your aura determines your first responses to people and situations and is a quicker and more sensitive gauge that many more rational faculties. The unease you sometimes feel in certain people's company may result from an aura that vibrates out of harmony with your own. Similarly, a sense of feeling immediately at ease with someone suggests that your aura resonates with theirs. This factor is particularly important when choosing a practitioner, for you are placing your well-being in his hands and this requires trust and openness.

Vibrational healing can be particularly beneficial when certain techniques and remedies are used in combination. It may therefore be a good idea to find a healer who has a broad

knowledge of vibrational healing and can formulate a combination of treatments.

COMBINING VIBRATIONAL THERAPIES

There is a current trend in complementary medicine to com-
bine the benefits of two or three different therapies, for example, herbalism and osteopathy. The same is true of vibrational
healing: the therapeutic benefits of colour, for instance, can be
augmented by sound, and a hands-on treatment such as acupressure may be complemented by the prescription of flower
essences. Crystals are increasingly being used by many practitioners to amplify their healing abilities.

METAFORM

Metaform treatment is a good example of how various vibrational therapies can be combined. Metaforms – chandeliers of
coloured pentagons – are the creation of Gregory Hoag, an
American healer who was inspired by visions of geometric patterns of energies.

In a typical treatment the patient lies beneath a metaform on a
mattress of copper, holding two crystals connected to it by copper wire. The patient is surrounded by an electromagnetic field
of energy. The practitioner may place crystals, gemstones or
flower essences on the pentagons to personalize the treatment.

During the treatment, energy movement may be felt as a tingling in certain areas of the body. At the end of a treatment a crystal bowl is sounded and the healing note reverberates through
the patient, helping to harmonize the energetic vibrations.

Metaform treatment appears to be particularly effective for
promoting a deep relaxation akin to meditation, releasing energy blockages, cleansing the aura and promoting self-awareness.

CASE STUDY

Melissa was a psychotherapist working in a busy practice. she was over-stressed and wanted her life to take a new direction, but did not know which path to follow. She decided to try a metaform treatment.

Flower essences for clarifying direction and purpose in life were prescribed in the first treatment. In the second treatment, Delph (dolphin) essence was indicated, which helps to bring knowledge from the past into the present. Crystal bowls for the third eye and heart chakras were sounded at the end of the session.

After her treatments Melissa had a strong desire to go to Hawaii to swim with the whales and dolphins, but to finance the trip she had to sell her flat. She decided to take the plunge and having done so, came into contact with the Hunna (Hawaiian shamans) and began working with them. She now feels she is on the right path and is fulfilling her purpose in life.

RESOURCES

ADDRESSES

COLOUR AND LIGHT THERAPIES

UK

Hygeia Studios, Brook House, Avening, Tetbury, Glos GL8 8NS

The International Association of Colour Therapy, c/o The
Institute for Complementary Medicine, 15 Tavern Quay,
Plough Lane, Surrey Quays, London SE16 1QZ

Aura-Soma, Deva Aura, Little London, Telford, Lincs LN9
6QL. Tel: 01507 533781, fax: 01507 533412

USA

Society for Light Treatment and Biological Rhythms (SLTBR),
PO Box 478, Wilsonville OR 97070. Tel: 503 694 2404

CRYSTAL THERAPY

Association of Crystal Healers Organisation (ACHO), 72
Pasture Road, Goole, East Yorkshire DN14 6HE. Tel/fax:
01405 769119

International College of Crystal Healing (ICCH), 46 Lower
Green Road, Esher, Surrey KT10 8HD. Tel: 0181 398 7252

FLOWER ESSENCES:
PRACTITIONERS, COURSES AND ESSENCES

UK

International Federation for Vibrational Medicine, Middle
Piccadilly, Holwell, near Sherborne, Dorset DT9 5LW. Tel:
01963 23028/23468

International Flower Essence Repertoire, The Working Tree,
Milland, near Liphook, Hants GU30 7JS. Tel: 01428
741572/741672, fax: 01428 741679

USA

Flower Essence Pharmacy at Centregees, 2007 NE 39th Ave,
Portland, OR 97212. Orders: 800 343 8693, Tel: 508 281 4906,
Fax: 503 284 7090

AUSTRALIA

Rainbows and Bridges, 68 Lynette Avenue, Warrandyte,
Victoria 3113, Australia. Tel:/fax: 61 398 44 2611

HOMEOPATHY

British Homeopathic Association, 27a Devonshire Street,
London W1N 1RJ

Society of Homeopaths, 2 Artisan Road, Northampton NN1 4H

PSYCHIC SURGERY

Stephen Turoff, The Miami Hotel, Princes Road, Chelmsford,
Essex CM2 9AJ. Tel: 01245 348325 (10 a.m. – 2 p.m.)

QI GONG

Chinese Heritage, 15 Dawson Place, London W2 4TH.
Tel: 0171 229 7187

The Confederation of Radionic and Radiesthetic Organisations
(CRRO), The Maperton Trust, Wincanton, Somerset BA9 8EH.
Tel: 01963 32651, fax 01963 32626

Radionic Association, Barelein House, Goose Green,
Deddington, Banbury, Oxon OX15 0SZ

REIKI

International Reiki Society, The Voice of the Reiki Community,
PO box 1867, Yeovil, Somerset. Tel: 01935 851170

SHEN TAO ACUPRESSURE

The Shen Tao School of Acupressure, Middle Piccadilly,
Holwell, near Sherborne, Dorset DT9 5LW. Tel: 01963 23468

SHIATSU

The Shiatsu Society of Great Britain, 14 Oakdeane Road,
Redhill, Surrey RH1 6HT

The British School of Shiatsu-Do, East-West Centre, 188 Old
Street, London EC1V 9BP

SOUND

Signature Sounds, Sharry Edwards, Bio Acoustics and
Signature Sounds USA, PO Box 706, Athens, Ohio 45701,
USA. Tel: (614) 592 5115, fax: (614) 592 6116

Elaine Thompson, The Unicorn Centre, 57 Hillhead,
Glastonbury, Somerset BA6 8AW. Tel: 01458 833238

CYMATICS

Peter Guy Manners, Bretforton Hall Clinic, Bretforton, Vale of
Evesham, Worcestershire. Tel: 01386 830918

DIGERIDOO

Contact Cyrung, tel: 0181 932 0494

SPIRITUAL HEALING

National Federation of Spiritual Healers, Old Manor Studio,
  Church Street, Sunbury-on-Thames, Middlesex TW16 6RG

VIBRATIONAL HEALING

RESIDENTIAL

Middle Piccadilly Natural Healing Centre, Holwell, near
  Sherborne, Dorset DT9 5LW. Tel: 01963 23468. For
  metaform, Shen Tao, subtle energetics/micromovement,
  flower remedies.

NON-RESIDENTIAL

The Hale Clinic, 7 Park Crescent, London W1N 3ME. Tel: 0171
  631 0604

GENERAL HEALING ORGANIZATIONS

The Confederation of Healing Organizations (CHO), Suite J,
  The Red and White House, 113 High Street, Berkhamsted,
  Herts HP4 2DJ

The British Complementary Medicine Association (BCMA)
  249 Fosse Road, Leicester LE3 1AE. Tel: 0116 2825 511, fax:
  0116 2825 611

Pullar, Philippa. *Spiritual and Lay Healing*, Penguin

Tansley, David V. *Radionic Healing: is it for you?* Element

Campbell, Don G. *The Roar of Silence*, Quest Books

Garfield, Laeh Maggie. *Sound Medicine*, Celestial Arts, California

Cochrane, Amanda and Callen, Karena. *Dolphins and their Power to Heal*, Bloomsbury

Shealy, C. Norma, ed. *The Complete Family Guide to Alternative Medicine*, Element

Reader's Digest Family Guide to Alternative Medicine, Reader's Digest Association

Liberman, Jacob. *Light, the Medicine of the Future*, Bear & Co, 1991

Harvey, Eliaina and Oatley, Mary Jane. *Acupressure Shen Tao*, Hodder & Stoughton, 1994

Gerber, Richard. *Vibrational Medicine*, Bear & Co, 1988

Harvey, Clare G. and Cochrane, Amanda. *The Encyclopedia of Flower Remedies*, Thorsons, 1995

Anderson, Mary. *Colour Healing*, Aquarian Press, 1979

Melody. *Love is in the Earth, a Kaleidoscope of Crystals*, Earth Love Publishers, 1991

The Shaman's Drum, no. 44, 1997, PO Box 311, Ashland, OR 97520, USA

Bryant, Alice and Phyllic Galde. *The Message of the Crystal Skull*, Llewellyn's New Age Series, 1989